Despite Anything

Short stories and other writings

Mark Whittaker

OZYMANDIAS BOOKS

Despite Anything by Mark Whittaker.
First edition (UK) published in 2004 by Ozymandias Books,
71A Colvestone Crescent, Dalston, London E8 2LJ (in association
with Helter Skelter Publishing).

Cover design by Mychael Gerstenberger, Malbuch, Berlin
Front cover print and vignettes in poetry section © Chris Pig 2004
Marbled paper, back cover and endpapers: Mark Whittaker
Interior design: Annabel Faraday
Typesetting: Caroline Walker
A big thankyou to Deena Omar and to Sean Body,
Helter Skelter Publishing
Printed in Great Britain by The Bath Press, Bath.

A CIP record for this book is available from the British Library.

ISBN 0-9547808-0-9

Distributed by NBN International

Despite Anything

MARAK

Edited by Adrian Whittaker

Mark Whittaker was born in Burton-on-Trent in 1956 and grew up in Blackheath, South-East London, where he first started to write poetry. After a degree in biochemistry at York University, he studied piano to performance level and ran a successful paper-marbling business in the town until a breakdown forced him to give it up in 1984. In the years immediately before, during and after the onset of his schizophrenic illness he wrote prolifically, and it is mainly from this period that this anthology is drawn. In 1987 he moved to Saffron Walden, near his parents, where he continued to write shorter prose pieces, meditations and poems, adopting the name 'Marak'. He died in 2003.

CONTENTS

INTRODUCTION

ark Whittaker's writing can not easily be categorised. You can spot a few influences here and there – Mervyn Peake undoubtedly, Dostoyevsky perhaps. At the heart of his writing, though, there are some recurring themes. Apart from some early poems, all the writing in this book stems from a period of intense productivity in the years immediately before, during and after the onset of his schizophrenic breakdown. What emerges most strongly for me is the sense of an intensely creative person with a fiercely individual world view trying to make sense of, and find hope and even humour in, a world from which he is profoundly alienated: a world at best unsettling, at times terrifying.

The short stories reflect this world view, leavened with a quirky humour. The protagonists are on the edge of society, like Philippe in *The Fugitive*, or the 'lunatics who think they are God' in *Restitution*. Then, perhaps influenced by Mark's background in biochemistry, there are the oddball scientists of *The Oracle Bones* and *The Biggest Memory In The World*, and ascetic figures searching for the purest expressions of beauty and truth such as Jaquel in *The Pearl Fisher*, Arkady in *A Seaside Story*, and the author himself in *Dream*. The gentle, compassionate treatments in *Giving* and *Love Story* act as a contrast to the other pieces in this section and assert an undimmed faith in the individual's power for good.

Mark identified strongly with people from the 'underclass', who take centre stage in his first book. The marginalised protagonists of *The Hunt For The Grail*, all based on York friends and acquaintances, band together into a dysfunctional and quarrelsome team to seek their respective nirvanas, each contributing according to their means and abilities. A very funny and well-observed novella, it also reaffirms Mark's faith in the individual.

The theme of making sense of a hostile world finds its most extensive and demanding expression in *Approach To The Threshold*. Here the 'action' takes place almost entirely within the head of the narrator, who invites us to join him as he experiments with characters and scenes in order to confront – and defeat – militarism in the shape of a tank. It was written three years before the events of Tianamen Square. At the same time, there are strong parallels with Mark's personal battle with what he termed 'mental dis-ease'.

The poems published here span most of Mark's life. The earliest, *House Of Cards*, though written when he was eight, foreshadows some of his adult themes. As a teenager, he was encouraged to write by the poet John Pudney; the romantic 'London' poems are playful and well-crafted, displaying an emergent personal voice. After moving to York, he really hit his stride as a poet. Coming from the same 'outsider' perspective as his fiction, his best work, as seen in *Fulford Cemetery, The City Is Alive With Worship* or *I Am A Stranger*, asserts itself through striking use of imagery and rhythm. Mark's poetry was the work he was proudest of and I think he would be delighted that it is now reaching a wider audience.

The Appendix includes a biography, an article on Mark's work as a marbler and some of his more recent pieces. Mark died in 2003.

Adrian Whittaker, June 2004.

Short Stories

A SEASIDE STORY

God howled through the keyhole and fell in large white flakes. It was winter. Arkady Nemesovitch sat in his room staring moodily out of the window. He had a single room to himself, a rented room. He could not afford more. But the room had a view of the sea, enough of an expanse to keep him calm and sometimes happy. Perhaps if he had found a place further inland he could have afforded somewhere bigger. He needed the sea. Besides, from this room he could hear the laughing clowns, busy in the 'amusements' at the sea front. This pleased him. His room was bare: a chair, a table, no possessions except for an expensive-looking tape recorder which rested on the table. Next to it was a loaf of bread and a piece of cheese. One of his hands toyed with a microphone.

Arkady had an unusual job, a job which not many people would ever think of. To call it a job is perhaps misleading as it provided extremely sporadic employment, but to Arkady it was a job, his lifetime work. He dealt in laughter. He produced and sold laughter for laughing automatons in glass cases. He produced laughter for everyone, but especially, like so many creative souls, he produced it to please himself.

He had started young. He had been considered bright at school but his lack of application had brought him castigation, and none of those pieces of paper which are considered so necessary to get on in life. His mother had despaired frequently. 'Whatever will become of our Arkady?' she would often ask.

'Don't worry Martha, he has a good star, see how he laughs. He will always fall on his feet,' his father would reply.

And so it was, after roaming the country for several years, living on tit-bits of work and goodwill, Arkady came to laughter. When he had started thirty years ago, he had been the only laughter man to be found; life, if not materially comfortable, was at least easy in this respect: no-one else could be found who could do it or who was prepared to try. The machine makers tried to establish their own laughters, but these were generally too self-conscious and folded up after a few snatches of laughter, or else their laughter had the wrong quality, it was too forced or too cracked, they failed to reach the correct level of hysteria. Arkady could do it perfectly.

For a while, trade had faltered as the manufacturers had started tickling their employees, but this had turned out not to be as conducive to the public good or generosity as Arkady's artful performances. So, for twenty years Arkady had ruled in his kingdom of laughter. However, after these twenty years there had come competition, and recently the more terrible threat of laughter concocted by sophisticated electronic synthesisers. Arkady's habits of laughter had changed to meet the changing circumstances.

There had been laughter which, he himself had been forced to admit, was almost as good as his own. He had been forced to experiment with new forms of laughter, 'novelty laughters' as they had become known in the trade. He had begun with puerile laughter, and this sold well but Arkady had been disgusted at himself for this cheapness. Cynical laughter had been quite fashionable in city areas and, similarly, evil laughter had been tried to considerable acclaim. But Arkady's heart had not been in these forms; he had become sad. All he had been able to do – which at least had given him a feeling of integrity – was to produce the laughter of despair and disillusionment. Directors of very modern plays had flocked to him. Who could have foreseen that these two obscure undergrounds would have met? Actors were trained to Arkady's tapes to laugh at existence or the moon. But Arkady could not bear this laughter forever. Laughing affected him for months if not years afterwards, and his growth was the accumulation of years of laughter inside him, tainted in the present by the laughter of the moment. He had fallen silent and brooded.

His silence had not been an empty one, however. Without words, almost unconsciously he had moved towards something new. With his experience of laughter of all kinds, what new laughter was possible? A laughter to be made possible by the laughter of despair and disillusionment, a laughter neither trite nor simple. Over the years his plan had developed. The laughter must be a laughter of the body, of the mind, of all that is in a person, but especially it would be of the spirit. It would be a life-affirming laughter which would raise people up, the kind of laughter which many people experience for a few seconds in their life, but which is then lost in the flurry of everyday trivia and probably forgotten. Words, yes! But how many of you can remember a laugh as freshly as it happened?

Much of these three years had been spent in meditation – the brooding had turned into something more positive – and, in between meditations, activities which would prepare him for this laughter. He went for walks along the cliff top, swam in the cold sea, immersed himself too in all texts he could think of as wise. He absorbed the religions of the world, from the teaching of Zoroaster to those of the animistic religions of Africa. He dwelt on all that was good and beautiful. He found that he could apply himself now that he had an end in mind, and took pleasure in his learning; for the first time in his life he was really alive. There would be no practising, no hesitation. One day he would switch on the tape recorder, and – laugh. At the end of the three years, in the autumn before I write these words, he had sat down at his table and smiled quietly for an hour and a third, switched on the machine, and there it had been, as hoped, as by now expected, The Laughter.

He had taken his machine along to the manufacturers and presented it. It had been played. The laughter swam and flew, dived, leapt for joy. Containing the earth, it soared high above the earth. It was a laughter like God. Its textures and inflections, riches and modulations – it was a symphony of laughter, or – no, that is too staid – it stood to laughter as a tree blowing in the wind stands to an artificial flower or a work of art. It was not art – it was life, and almost beyond life, the life that is only glimpsed on rare occasions. The listeners had been astounded. One of them had started to cry. The others had looked on with understanding. There had been a long silence when the laughter had finished. 'You are a genius!' the manufacturers had said in a whisper. A discussion had followed. What automaton could bear this laughter appropriately? Perhaps a clown, but the message would be too complicated. A sage in a loincloth was suggested, but this was felt inappropriate too. Probably a glass case, elaborately decorated with nothing in it. Perhaps a whole room dedicated to this laughter, one in every town for the refreshment and education of the townspeople. Plans proliferated. A decision has still not been taken. The laughter has been bought, but there has been doubts as to its acceptability, fears that it might be found offensive, reminding people too much of their imperfections.

Arkady Nemesovitch now sits in his room, as you have seen him, brooding once more. He has accomplished all that he can accomplish in life or at least in laughter; he is at a loss. He has thought of going into tears, but crying at beauty has more to be experienced than heard. I think that after he has got over this period in another month or two he will come back to this laughter, lift it gently back within himself, and live with it for the rest of his life. This is what I hope – there is often sadness after a great creative effort. Arkady if you hear me, please do not lose this laughter, you don't have to speak it aloud. Keep this laughter in the world Arkady, we need your laughter, do it for us.

27/8/1986

THE ORACLE BONES

The Balthambray Phrenological Society had convened for an extraordinary meeting. Already I am betraying my renegade status, as the society no longer exists under this name. The National Phrenological Society of Great Britain, of which this group had been a part, had been disbanded a number of years before. Its demise had been commented on in the press, an occasion for much wry humour and celebration of the loss of one more source of the incorrigible crank from our great culture; the truth, however, is more startling. Following the analysis of the skulls of a number of prominent geniuses, (some unrecognised, such as the – by us – celebrated night watchman of Bumblehead) the society had made the discovery of what has eluded humankind for millennia, the meaning and purpose of life. Renegade as I am, I respect the society enough not to break my vow of secrecy in this matter. This no doubt will be felt to be unfortunate, but we have our reasons. The society that now met in Balthambray was known vaguely, if at all, as some inner circle of Freemasons, and this belief was encouraged.

The meeting, at which I was present, was held in the upper part of a large warehouse-like place of the last century, within the upper part, in a room measuring perhaps twenty-five feet by fifteen. The congregation (for with our great discoveries it seems fitting to describe our assembly in this way) consisted for the most part of elderly men and women. Here and there were the eager, earnest faces of our younger members, conduits for the great truths to slip along into the meandering enormity of the future. Many of these people had with them in carrier bags the skulls of their grandfathers, mothers, or other ancestors (one might wonder how they came to possess them); reverence to one's ancestors was especially great among our number.

Our leader stood at the front of the room at a lectern, before the congregation. If it seems odd that so obscure a place as Balthambray should spawn a leader, let me warn you in a true if hackneyed phrase that Balthambray exists within each and every one of you. Our truths are universal, and each one of you possesses in some sense our truths. Our leader in his black formal dress and crown of grey hair raised his hand for silence.

'Long live the forty-two divisions.'

'Long live the forty-two divisions,' came the murmured assent.

The forty-two divisions refer to the forty-two regions of the skull which in their physical character express the nature of the mind within. I may tell you that in a humorous radio programme called 'The Hitch-Hiker's Guide to the Galaxy', a computer set to find the answer to the question of 'Life, the Universe and Everything' came up (after a number of centuries) with the answer 'Forty-two'. The author of this programme was one of us. It is perhaps too unlikely to be a coincidence that the number of the house I live in is also forty-two.

'Let us turn our attention tonight to that region of the skull reflecting the moral, ethical and spiritual sentiments, partly in the frontal lobes and partly in the parietal lobes. Specifically let us turn our attention to the region within this, known as the region of Wonder to Doctor Gall, and as Marvellousness to Doctor Spurzheim at a later date. It is found in the inner side of the second frontal convolution. It adjoins Veneration on the inside edge, ideally on the lower edge, and Imitation in front. I have been researching this area for a number of years, indeed it is my speciality. What has been, to the best of my knowledge, overlooked since the eighteenth century, is it that it is essentially the region of dreams. From a comparison of the skulls of known dreamers and undreamers, it has been my privilege to discover that full development of this area accrues only to those who have dreamt. Friends, let us dream tonight, let us dream the great dream which I will unfold to you.

'Here before me is a skull. You have seen many skulls before and they have not tested your patience. But there is a skull of particular significance.'

Here our leader broke off with a short cough which was a characteristic of him. He grasped effortlessly the skull of such weighty import and held it aloft.

'It is a very ancient skull, the skull of a caveman, found by myself in a cave on the shores of Lake Edward in Nigeria. It has been authenticated, I assure you, there is no doubt of its millions, of years that is. It is the skull of a male ancestor of ours. Perhaps all of us living in this room are the descendants of this once-being.'

Our leader went on to enumerate its features.

'But friends!' – Here his voice leapt upward a fraction from its customary evenness. 'Friends, I play with you. What is it that stares you in the eyes? That is, besides my own.'

Here his usual exactitude took over.

'It is that this caveman, this once-being of so many millennia, this being – dreamt.'

He said the word 'dreamt' in a breathless whisper. There was a gasp from the audience.

'And if that is not enough, my friends, let me astonish you further. Who has thought of looking at the inside of the skull?'

Here he paused.

'I have looked inside of the skull.'

There was another gasp from the audience.

'On the inside of the region of Wonder there is, under the microscope, a great deal of space. This space is lined and grained in a most complicated way. What have I found? I have found, firstly, four depressions in the form of legs, secondly an undulating shape which undoubtedly represents the torso and rear quarters of a bison. Further searches have revealed to me a head, tail and four wings. Ladies and gentleman, this simple being dreamt persistently of a four-winged bison with green teeth, although it is not quite clear whether the green is an algal deposit. Ladies and gentlemen, we dream of what is important to us.'

He broke off here and went into an unknowable reverie, perhaps a dream, in which the audience in a sense shared. After a minute or two he sprang back into the fray.

'But! Here is a further wonder. In this region of the skull's interior, there is a distinctly two-dimensional representation of an oblong cuboid. At one end of it is a dot with a line in front of it, and then in front of this an area stippled with many dots. Ladies and gentleman, friends, what was this a dream of? It was a dream of us, here tonight. Friends, we were predestined to make this discovery. This caveman, in his loneliness, his inarticulacy, how could he communicate with us today? He found a way, my friends, he found a way. Ladies and gentlemen, we have done a marvellous thing tonight. We have liberated a dream. We must wish and dream for the future, my friends. This is how we must save the world!'

8/8/86

THE PEARL FISHER

Jaquel sat by his pool. He always sat by his pool, this particular pool. What made this pool of particular interest to him was the oyster which lay on its floor. In the oyster there might be a pearl. This was why Jaquel sat here, and had sat here for over eight years, nearly naked in the sun and dying slowly, the healthy dying of a great old age. Just one more time in his life he would dive, just once, and the pearl would be his.

Beside him, in a sun brilliant enough to force some gleam even out of its rusty surface, was the knife, ready to prise open the oyster. Rusty as it was, its edge was honed beautifully, the first work of every morning. The knife was a gift from an islander, the bequest of some long-forgotten ancestor of his. He was giving up pearls, he had said. He was going to work in a disco in the capital. The knife had been accepted gratefully and with a feeling of pride. Pride both in the magic conferred on the implement by age, and also in the fact that he would continue the struggle which the younger man had given up.

It was a struggle, a quiet and courtly struggle, a struggle of mind, expectation, hope, despair, all was concentrated on the oyster at the bottom of the pool. But even this is too wide a description of Jaquel's focus. His focus was more abstract, more abstract than the material greed that might be the conclusion of a bystander: his focus was on a theoretical pearl, a hypothetical pearl; his struggle was in the realm of theory. As with all theories the emotions were involved, but this theory was life to Jaquel. The oyster was like a prism: through it went the light of concentration, which was split into the many colours of thought and feeling. There was even darkness in this spectrum, but only a little.

'Hello Jaquel. What are you doing today?' the newcomer laughed.
Jaquel smiled.
'It will be a fat one, Jaquel, to be sure.'
Jaquel accepted his words, was willing to accept them as prophecy.

Jaquel rarely spoke, but today he would, he was near the end of his quiet adventure; the end, whatever it would be, was almost as good as achieved.

At first the words crackled in his dry innards which were unaccustomed to bearing them. 'Meleagrina Margaritifera,' he pronounced, looking into the eyes of Maurien Duval with wonder.

'What's that?'

Jaquel pointed to the oyster in the pool.

'Don't you ever watch the fish there, the one that glitters? At least it moves.'

Jaquel ignored the question. 'Do you remember Morbihan?' he asked.

'In Brittany, yes.'

'I used to work the oysters there. We worked hard, but I started to grow old. I wanted something better than that.'

'So you came here.'

'Yes, at first I dived with Amola, the others, but I never got a pearl. They told me to go. Now I watch this one. I know I'm right.'

'You are a one, Jaquel. It might be the Holy Grail for you.' Maurien looked humorously into his eyes. Jaquel was lost in thought. 'Well, I must be going Jaquel, I've work to do!'

Jaquel remained in his reverie. Maurien smiled to himself, turned and walked off. Jaquel came out of his thought in time to see Maurien disappear amongst the trees. What Maurien had said was already lost to him. He almost deduced, from the direction of Maurien's walking, that he had been with him a few minutes earlier.

He stretched his arms and worked his back muscles. He continued the progress into liveliness by standing up, taking off his ragged shorts, and, without pausing, jumping into the pool. He swam, as much as the pool's confines would allow. Here he was happy, closer to the oyster, the pearl. He did this every day, without knowing why he did it. Perhaps if he had thought, he would have said to himself that he needed to keep his physical powers for the time when he would fetch the oyster. But, here he was in the same element as his prize, in the same element with his wishes, his pent-up joy, working with them a kind of magic on the oyster. He climbed out and lay in the sun. Few people came this way, and those who did would think nothing of seeing Jaquel naked, except perhaps for a worry that he might be dead.

Dressed, the day passed timelessly, therefore quickly for him. It passed like a painting, for no movement disturbed the scene. The minute swaying of a flower might have blurred a photograph of the day, but ever so slightly. As the sun set, Jaquel stood up once more and looked along the deep narrow gully which led from the pool to the sea. The sea was necessary to him as well. All of nature was concentrated in the oyster he watched; his physical body, he barely counted; his mind, like the pearl, was an abstraction. He walked to his hut not far away. Here he would prepare his meal. The necessities of life meant little to him, they were abundant and free. Fruits grew on the trees and bushes, roots in the ground, and a box of matches might be had without payment from Amola, his nearest neighbour, a mile away.

The days passed in this way for almost another nine months. The occasional typhoon disturbed him little. Whatever its force, Jaquel, his hut, the oyster, they remained. One day when he went to his pool he found the oyster had gone. He had settled down in his usual position by the pool and looked. He had seen no oyster, but still he had looked. It took him till midday to realise that the oyster had gone. Silently he had turned his back on the pool and gone back to his hut, where he lay in his hammock for three days without eating. On the third day, thoughts broke the silence of his mind. At first he thought it had been stolen. But I am too old to cry, too old to rage, he thought. Perhaps a pig has eaten it. This was a better thought. If he could find the pig and kill it… But there were so many pigs. He lapsed again into silence.

On the fourth day he reluctantly got up and went back to his pool. He stared into it from a rock which jutted out into the pool. As he stared, he noticed the fish which lived in the pool. It darted and twisted, lazed. Why had he never noticed the fish before? He gazed at the fish, entranced, with growing admiration. Maurien had said something about the fish ages ago. What had he said? He had not seen Maurien for a long time now. As he looked at the fish he experienced something like rapture. Here was his new life – it had been there all the time. But was this his real life? What would happen when the fish died or went away? After a moment's thought the answer came. Why! Then he would have himself.

14/8/86

DREAM

All of us have secrets, and many of them are so secret that they are secret even to ourselves – the thousands of dreams we have in our lifetime and cannot recall, secrets often of an extreme nature. I will share a secret with you, a dream which has not yet taken place; that is, it has not yet been transformed by dreaming into reality. This dream is already an outward one, even mundane. To me it is precious.

One summer he packs up his rucksack and travels to the North. He is going to walk through the Highlands, first by the sea and then amongst the mountains. He takes with him only a bag of porridge and another of coffee. These and some sachets of soup are all he takes by way of supplies. He walks along a rocky coastline where, he imagines, no-one has been for years, perhaps ever. At night in his tent he fancies he hears the seals calling amongst the rocks in the mouth of the cove. He sees birds of prey, rabbits, flowers he has never seen before. The burden of civilised living lightens and he begins to feel physically lighter. After the first few days his limbs have loosened up, and now he feels that he could keep walking forever. He stops now and then at night, merely to enjoy the surroundings and because sleep is habitual. He walks for many miles without seeing any human being, only the signs of humankind amongst the debris washed up on the beaches. As he continues he grows closer and closer to tears; it is so beautiful. But if he were to start crying he would never stop. Words cease to have any meaning for him, he does not use them even in his thoughts, he *knows* what to do. Occasionally a word, a sentence comes into his head and he speaks it aloud, but it seems strange to him.

He turns inland across a flattened area before the mountains. In this part of the journey he meets the only people he will meet. In the early morning one day he meets some travellers passing round a bottle of cider. They greet him. He tells them that there are some rabbits further back

but they will have to run fast if they want some breakfast. He leaves them
for the mountains.

In the mountains he is almost overcome by the beauty within himself,
the beauty he absorbs from his surroundings. Physically he almost ceases
to have an existence. He doesn't eat for three days, not because he is denying himself, but because he has forgotten himself, he has no need of sus-
tenance, his spirit keeps him on.

One day he climbs a mountain. He comes to a cliff edge on the way to
its summit. Over the edge of this cliff there is a drop for hundreds of feet.
He stands at the cliff edge; he has no fear of this. His gaze comes nearer to
himself, to the cliff on which he stands. By his feet is a large and perfect
crystal or amethyst lying loose on the cliff top. He stares at it, surprised.
Perfect, it has almost the form of something created by humankind rather
that thrown up by nature, but it has a greater perfection than the too obvious forms of humankind. It mocks the perfection of human creation; the
old earth laughs. He bends down to look at it more closely. He reaches
out to touch it but takes his hand back. He stands up and looks at the
amethyst for a long time. Finally he turns to go. He leaves it there. Now
he will go home; he has found what the purpose of his journey was.

28/08/1986

THE BIGGEST MEMORY IN THE WORLD

When I have to spend a night alone, I often pass the time by telling myself the story of my life. I lock the house, lie on our bed and play it through as many times as it takes to get me to sleep.

It falls into two parts, Before and After. Before is sad. No-one would think, to look at me now, that I could ever have been as desperate as I was when I found myself driven to analysis at the age of twenty four. The source of the problem was in a universal human condition, forgetfulness. Most of us have, at one time or another, cursed the poor thing we call memory, and wished there was some way to avoid the terrible loss of some incident or fact, perhaps important, perhaps trivial, which we wanted to keep alive in our mind. The innate inadequacy of human memory doesn't however lead us one and all to a velvet couch in a darkened room; I have had all my life an extraordinary awareness of this particular human frailty, and a powerful desire to overcome it. The many battles I lost on the way to winning this war constitute the part of my story which I call Before, and I'll review them now.

From the moment of my birth, I knew that things were slipping away from me, and I hated it. The cord was cut and tied, and I began to cry. Loss. With every new impression that forced itself upon me, it seemed an existing one was wiped away. I learned the feel of the breast and forgot the architecture of the womb. There was a constant leak, a spiritual incontinence that matched the bodily one, but which no-one cared about nor even seemed to notice. As unable to express my misery as I was to keep any kind of physical record, I developed in my first month a habit of never releasing anything I held until it was wrested from my grip. My hands carry scars to this day (so would my mother's if she was alive), and despite using them less than ever they remain phenomenally strong.

I learned to write at the age of three and immediately started keeping diaries. I used green notebooks, hard-covered, with creamy blank pages. Soon I was buying them wholesale, even though my writing was and is neat and extremely small.

It was a stop-gap, but no solution. There was not always the opportunity to write when I needed to; my father prohibited me it at mealtimes and other family occasions, my teachers threatened to confiscate it, my companions fell silent as I reached for my pen. I became secretive and was often forced to depend on the treachery of organic memory to carry my impressions until I was free to record them, often late into the night, only to wake with a debt of dreams. I grew increasingly lonely, for lack of sleep made me nervous and unhealthy-looking; I must have seemed cold and absent-minded, so intent was I on the constant effort to recall.

I took to carrying a small cassette recorder so as to unobtrusively capture at least the verbal part of my more significant experiences – notably the break-up of my affair with Anna. A lonely soul herself, she sought me out at every opportunity, and though I appreciated the company I resented it for distracting me from my memories. Her discovery of the tape recorder was largely instrumental in the bitterness that ensued, and definitely responsible for her wanton destruction, by fire, of twenty volumes, amounting to almost the entire three months of our doomed affair. That loss led directly to my first appointment with Francesca in the shuttered front room of 69 Lime Mews.

Despite an initial scepticism that amounted almost to despair, no sooner had I settled myself on the couch than I burst into tears. 'She didn't want me to remember,' I gasped.

'You can remember here,' Francesca said. 'What is the earliest incident you recall?'

I replied instantly: 'I am sitting in a highchair holding an egg. My mother has her back to me and is cutting something with a big knife. The egg is cool, pale beige and speckled with brown. I love the egg. Suddenly my mother is screaming. I don't understand. She reaches for the egg. My hand clenches. Suddenly there is no egg. It's tuned into something cold and wet. My mother slaps me then cries. I love the egg and I have lost it…'

Week after week Francesca took me back, behind, between my existing memories. To my delight I found that with her help I could remember incidents from my earliest years which I had no notion had ever even been forgotten! Furthermore, my silver cassette recorder sat openly between us on the table, and we would even pause while I changed its batteries. I had found a place where memory was sought and valued as I sought and valued it, and I began to lose the sense of being a creature apart from the rest of humanity. Soon I was attending every day of the week, and working long hours at the office in order to pay Francesa's fee.

I developed a frightening dependence on her. I imagined accidents claiming her. I wondered what I would do if she were to take to her bed one night and die in her sleep, or even wake up one morning and decide to retire. I phoned her at home, I waited outside her door, I checked on her comings and goings as if she was a golden key that at any time might be lost or stolen from me, and for many months she bore it with complete equanimity.

'Gabriel,' she said to me at the beginning of our three hundred and sixth appointment. Her voice was very low, and rasped from smoking Turkish cigarettes in the brief pauses between appointments. Their bitter smell always hung in the room, which over the years had taken on a brownish hue. 'Gabriel – I would like you to turn off your machine today.' No sooner were the words uttered than I leapt from the couch, seized the cassette recorder and clutched it to my chest. Francesca didn't move, and showed as ever no expression on her shadowy face. My fingers had made chaotic smears in the thick dust that coated the table and I fixed my eyes on them so as to avoid her relentless stare. My teeth clenched together, my heart seemed to rock the room and with each beat the muscles of my body tightened, tightened until I sat with each of them pitted equal against its opposite, utterly locked. If I could have moved, I would have fled at once; as it was, I remained a prisoner minute after minute, until Francesca broke the silence: 'The hour is over. This has been a very valuable session; from now on, our work will be much faster.' So completely, so terribly was I in her power that only then did my limbs begin to loosen.

'After such a powerful regression, I dare say you will leave here, cured, within a year.'

For the first time I say the hint of a smile on her face. 'Cured?' I asked, thinking only of how at home I would slip the cassette into my stereo and listen for a whole hour to the awesome beat of my heart, pure terror, the bodily essence of an overpowering experience caught forever.

'Cured of your obsession with memory,' Francesca said gently. 'When that's gone, you'll walk free.'

The clock struck with its felt-dulled ping and I found I could stand and walk to the door. 'You didn't understand,' I said. She gazed at me blankly, and reached for her cigarettes. Someone was waiting in the lobby outside.

I was shaking so much when I reached home that it took me several minutes to slip the key into the lock. I poured myself half an inch of brandy, turned on the cassette, slid the volume up to full, lay on the floor and closed my eyes. Francesca's opening words filled the room and were followed by a brief eruption of the kind of noise you hear if you press your hands hard over your ears and then remove them. Waiting for the beat of my own fearful heart I became calmer. There was a sharp click, and then the hiss of silence: in my panic I had been clumsy enough to switch the recorder off.

Of course, I never returned to Francesca, who had so casually with a few words robbed me both of herself and of what she could do for me. In the years that followed, all that kept me from suicide was the thought that I had come so close, and, surely, one day I would find what I needed, if only I kept on looking. I am fortunate indeed, that someone was looking for me as well.

It was on the front page of *The Times*:

Fight Forgetting:
Medical Science Can give YOU The Biggest Memory In The World.

I knew it was what I'd been looking for all my life, every single second and minute and hour of thirty-eight years. I ran to the nearest phone. I was the only person to answer the advertisement, or rather, the only suitable person. Obviously, the idea of surgery puts most people off, and brain surgery at that. It worried me too, but by then I would have done anything.

Doctor Leach's office at the Humana Hospital was air-conditioned, evenly lit and carpeted in white. There was an atmosphere of confidence and optimism about the place, and about the doctor himself. His unlined face exuded health, and the white coat scarcely concealed an extremely athletic physique. We faced each other man to man across the spotless desk.

'The procedure is not without an element of risk,' he told me. 'We feel however that there will be a substantial number of people, like yourself, who would consider implantation worthwhile. We at the Humana are pioneers in the field, and our team of surgeons is second to none.' Between us on the desk he placed an object the size of a two-penny piece, black, laced with a spiralling tracery of silver.

'That's it,' he said. 'The Biggest Memory In The World.' Unable to contain myself, I reached for it, but he gripped my wrist, twisted it warningly and pulled me forward over the table. He tapped the back of my skull. 'A small segment of bone will be removed here, and the memory inserted into the lower part of the brain where sensory inputs meet the interpretative faculty. The bone will be replaced, and it will take about a week for it to stabilise and the outer membrane of the brain to heal.' On the table next to the Memory he placed what looked like a miniature pocket calculator.

'The control,' he said, 'will fit in your wallet and attract no attention at all. Very simple to use. The basic functions: 1 Record, 2 Play, 3 List, 4 Review, 5 Pause, 6 Stop – plus functions 1 to 4 at accelerated speed. Accelerated Review you will find particularly useful if you want, for example, to present a simple account of any aspect of your life over a period of years. It will move major point to major point in chronological order, presenting you with a ready made narrative. 10 is an Escape key, which is for use only by your medical advisors in the unfortunate event of you becoming terminally ill; it has been designed to give you the opportunity to spend your last hours or minutes in a memory loop that will allow you to relive again and again the most cherished moment of your life. To the side, the plus sign, which allows the admission of memories you may have kept elsewhere prior to implantation, and the minus sign, this will erase a memory, and,' he smiled, 'from what you have told me, I imagine you will probably want to avoid its use. It can be disabled if you wish.' I put my house on the market and was admitted the next day.

I felt little discomfort. Of course, I hadn't bargained for the immense labour and extra cost of transcribing all my other records on to the new memory. However, as Doctor Leach pointed out, think how much worse it would have been had the marvellous technology that made it possible not existed! Now that the task is complete, the last green book burned, the last tape reused, I am transformed. I am happier than I have ever been, and I can truly say that the suffering of my search has already been amply repaid by what I have attained. This is the part of my story I call After. The happy end, the treasure at the foot of the rainbow, the Grail, my very own golden key. It makes up for the sadness of the part I call Before. Few people, I know, get so exactly what they want as I have done, and of those, fewer still can keep it as long as they would like to.

I've gone from strength to strength. Witness the vast improvement of my performance at work, achieved simply by pressing button number 1 on arrival in the office. Nothing escapes me, no name is forgotten, no detail neglected. My rise through the ranks can only be described as meteoric, yet I have achieved all this without experiencing the slightest stress, without missing a second's sleep. I have the confidence of infinite recall, and against common expectation, my social life has at the same time developed a richness and a glitter I never dared expect. I have a reputation for gaiety, for spontaneity – I feel like a god. I am free to experiment, I've had more women in the past few years than most men have in a lifetime, and now, now I have Becky almost every night of the week. Even when, as now, she isn't here, I can press Play and remember us together, exactly as it was, and in the moment's perpetual present tense.

I can remember: our first meeting. We are introduced at a cocktail party, and I am instantly, powerfully aroused. In response, her face and figure are that of a fashion idol, slender, smooth-skinned, pale, pout-lipped, wide eyed – but alert; as she speaks, this almost inhuman beauty is constantly interrupted, broken then reformed as each expression paints itself delicately on her face. Her beauty is the finest canvas, perfect, accepting even the lightest touch and allowing it to remain discrete. She is in fact the most desirable person in the world, not only beautiful but also intelligent, sensitive and warm-hearted. Tonight she has to leave early for another appointment, but before she goes I run my hand down her bare arm from shoulder to wrist, link my fingers against hers and kiss her softly on the lips, pressing my tongue against hers as a promise of things to come. She prises her fingers away. Tears spring to my eyes. It is almost too much to bear. I rub condensation from the window with my sleeve, watch her climb into a taxi, then sink into a chair. My friends gather round me. 'What's the matter, Gabriel?' they ask.

'I'm in love,' I reply.

I can remember our second meeting, the first time we made love. She comes to my house, wearing a dress of thin silk. As soon as the door is closed and locked I slide her skirt to her waist and slip my hand to her sex. It is wet, enormous: she wants me. Still holding her, I pull the dress over her head. Already I know that this is the memory I will choose if I am lucky enough to die lucid and Doctor Leach is there to press Escape for me.

'Stand still,' I say, 'I want to remember.' Everything, the slow curve of her back, the neat twist of her calves, the roughness of secret hair, the weight of her breasts, the colour of her eyes. I lead her to bed. She lies on her side and I watch her for a long time before I touch.

At the slightest movement her lids lower and a sheen of sweat breaks out on both our bodies; she smells of ripe apples and tastes of wine. The prints of my fingers are on her, white then red. She cries out. Time and again I feel the pulse of her climax about me, and because I want to keep her here, like this, for ever, because I want the longest possible memory of this night, it is only as dawn breaks that I explode into fulfilment.

'So what's your secret?' Becky asks, playing with my hair.

'Happiness,' I reply lazily.

'Yes,' she says, 'but what's the secret of that?' So perfect is the trust I feel that without hesitation I tell her that I have the Biggest Memory In The World.

'I don't believe it,' she laughs. I let her feel the slight depression on the back of my skull. I show her the remote. I allow her to press Select, then Play, and I relive for her the experience of my mother leaving me when I was nine, how I wandered through the empty house and eventually found a sealed envelope smelling of her – but it was addressed to my father and there was no word for me. How I slipped into her bedroom and sat at her dressing table, watching my face turn to water in the glass. Wanting something of her, I plucked at her abandoned hairbrush, gathering a tangle of auburn hairs; the sharp bristles slid under my pink and white nails and minute drops of blood fell on the lace mat below... When it's over, there are tears in both our eyes and Becky takes me in her arms.

'You poor darling,' she says, 'play me another one.' It's like coming home. I know that in time I will play her all my memories, and she will know me, truly, deeply as no-one, not even Franscesca, has ever done before.

I can remember: relaxing in the afterglow of playing Becky a charming memory of the moment I learned to ride a red bicycle. We are lying on a deserted beach, palm trees waving behind us, the sea ahead. Becky's skin has tanned to an exquisite honey colour with just a hint of pink. The fine hairs on her arms are brightest blonde.

'This is amazing,' she says, digging her hand into the warm sand, letting it slip slowly between her fingers. 'I'm sure as hell I'll remember this.' We laugh together, for the word *remember* has become a delightful private joke, especially since I have been encouraging her to overcome her fear of surgery and improve her memory. I have offered to pay for the operation, but she still refuses. *You have enough for the two of us*, she always says. I take a sip from my cocktail, play her my memory of the first time we made love, and watch her eyes darken with longing. Out bodies anointed with sun oil, glide over each other. I ask, 'Will you marry me Becky?'

'Oh, yes,' she replies.

I can remember: us sitting side by side at the head of a long table set out in a flowery meadow by the upper reaches of the Thames. We pour champagne into each other's mouths, everyone cheers. I know I am envied, but hand in hand with that envy goes a kind of appreciation – we are right for each other, perfect. I watch a small trail of champagne run down Becky's throat, imagine it running between her perfect breasts. Her eyes shine. Her veil is thrown back over her hair, the bouquet of orchids is beside her plate. I have not been so happy since the day I woke up in the hospital and knew I had the Biggest Memory In The World.

I can remember: standing in the bay window of our bedroom, lit only by a single bedside lamp. I kiss her, sliding the straps of her night-dress from her shoulders.

'Please,' she says, touching my hand, 'Gabriel, please, play your memory of the first time we made love.'

'You really should get one of your own,' I tease, and let her press the button herself.

I can remember: we've drunk coffee and eaten bitter chocolate with cream. Our guests are quiet, the rooms lit by the embers of the fire.

'You're a lucky man, Gabriel,' Alan my UK manager says as Becky comes in with brandy and a tray of glasses.

'Ah – Gabriel's secret is that he has the Biggest Memory In The World,' says Becky as she sits down beside Alan and the woody smell of cognac fills the room, 'haven't you darling? Show them, Gabriel, I'm sure they'd love to see.' I get out the control, and explain how it works. The company president is most intrigued.

'A scaled-down version of this would be of immense value to some of the company executives. What do you say, Alan, eh? Wouldn't be easy to sell implantation though. Perhaps a clip-on or plug-in version could be developed, Gabriel, if we were to invest…'

'Play them a memory,' interrupts Becky, reaching across for my hand in her eagerness, 'play them the first time, you know…' Afterwards, there's a profound silence in the room. Becky is leaning back with her eyes closed.

'Sir, I'll have one!' Alan says to the president, and we both look at Becky, only the movement of her breath disturbing her stillness, the perfect beauty of her face in repose. I long for us to be alone.

I can remember: There's a bird singing outside.

'I don't think I'm happy,' Becky says.

'Darling, what do you want?' I rush to dry her tears. She buries her face in the pillow, I try to ease it away, tell her the tears make no difference, she will always be beautiful to me. 'How can I help? Shall I play you our memory?' She clutches the pillow even harder, mutters something I can't hear, there's a long pause, and then she releases her grip. 'Here,' I say, slipping the control into her hand, 'it's always there. You know you can play it any time you want.'

I slept well. This morning, she's back and I know it's going to be another perfect day, so I feel for my control and press Record. We're having breakfast in the conservatory. The coffee's thick and pungent, the year's first sunshine falls on our table, drenching everything in gold.

'Have you noticed how my face has changed?'

'No,' I say, 'I don't think it has. Your hair's different of course. It suits you like that.' I notice my heart's beginning to beat faster, and set the coffee cup down. I think how I should look after my body, or else it will certainly wear out before my Memory does!

'Things change, Gabriel,' she says carefully. 'I'm really not happy. There's something missing.'

'What?' I ask, alarmed. 'You can have anything you want. You have your work. Do you want to have a – ?'

'No,' she says, 'it's not that. I haven't been happy since we married, not really. It's got worse and worse.' This, I know and can *prove*, is ridiculous.

'Nonsense,' I reply. 'You know we have been blissfully happy.'

'Even before…' she continues as if I hadn't spoken, 'even before I wasn't. We shouldn't have. If only you hadn't kept playing that memory…'

'Remember the beach in Hawaii?' I interrupt, aware still of my chest, the accelerated beat, the skips and stumbles. 'We made love by the sea.' I reach for my control to play it for her.

'Stop,' she says. 'Listen. I don't care what you've got on that little chip inside your head. The sand got inside me and it hurt for days.'

'That's just not true. Becky, I demand that you let me play that memory.' She sits stony-faced as I play it through, takes a sip of her coffee. I am still tender from the experience and want to take her in my arms.

'So what?' she says.

'But that was what happened.'

'I don't care! You and your memories. There's more to life. Anyway, that's your memory. I was just in it. I liked it for a while, but it wasn't ever mine and I don't want it any more.'

'You could have your own if you…'

'I don't want to. Things change. Even memories. People too.'

'You fell in love with my memory,' I say, my cheeks hot, my eyes suddenly tight in their sockets.

'Maybe I did. But it hasn't lasted. I'm sick of it. All you need is your fucking memory but I'm different.'

'Stop it Becky. You sound just like Anna! You're forgetting! Everything – the first time, the second, the beach, the wedding the dinner party, the nights – let me play you…'

'Too damn right I am!' she yells. 'Listen Gabriel, I *want* to forget!' She tries to pull the control from my hand. It's smallness makes it difficult to grip. I'm terrified it will be broken. We stand opposite each other over the table, prising at each other's fingers.

'Let go, you bastard,' she growls, and bends her head, teeth bared.

'Let me just play you the first time, the first time,' I beg. She closes her teeth over my thumb. The pain is unbearable. She frees her index finger. I can see the neat crescent of marks her teeth have made. 'Stop! Stop!' I cry.

Becky looks down, hesitates, chooses. My voice is shrill as a child's: 'Please! Let me play you the first time!' On the nail of her finger, shell-pink from the flesh pressed underneath, a speck of white like a full stop. Did she always have raw edges where the nail digs skin? Bitten edges, a torn cuticle?

'Becky!'

We look each other in the face. I see now that she has changed. Her eyes are fierce as they never have been before and they are brown whereas I always thought they were blue.

'Becky!'

She presses Escape.

I always thought they were blue.

I always thought they were blue.

RESTITUTION

Through a warehouse of marble pillars a man could be seen, sitting bolt upright in a leather chair. In front of him was a leather-topped desk on the far side of which another chair, similar to his own. The pillars were less densely clustered in the region of the desk, and to one side of it was a wall, bare except for the buttressing of three plinths on which, separately, were two objects and a garment. These were a sceptre, an orb (apparently made of gold), and a purple cloak. The man, the pillars, the objects and the garments together constituted the consultation room of the busy 'Kailserlichesklinikum Für Irren Die Sich Für Gott Halten'. ★ The consultant was dressed in a black suit and black tie. He was thin and gaunt. His bony fingers lay motionless on the cover of a large notebook which was on the desk in front of him.

A long, gravelled drive led to the clinic through an avenue of tall poplar trees. At intervals along the drive were notices with large lettering: 'Trust in the Lord', 'Judge not and ye shall not be judged', ' Know that I am God'; there were many messages. From the gateway a coach and horses could be seen at the far end of the avenue in front of the building. A figure stood by the coach, his arms raised in the air. After a few moments he flung himself to the ground and appeared to be kissing the earth. A costumed figure materialised beside him, helped him up, and led him into the building.

In an ante-room there were a number of cubicles for the clients. These were small but luxurious, and soundproofed. They guarded against the possibility of jealousy, and were a means of avoiding the brawls that had broken out in the early days amongst rival gods.

An old man was brought into the presence of the consultant and given a seat. He sat looking down at the desk, fiddling with his fingers. 'What

★ *Imperial Clinic for Lunatics who Think they are God*

did the budgerigar with no teeth say?' asked the consultant.

The client looked at the consultant eagerly. 'I don't know,' he said. 'I will succeed.'

The old man cackled. The consultant looked pleased. 'Good,' he said. 'And what is your name?'

'Izalbaum Diskau.'

'Good. That is promising.'

'Am I doing well?'

'Yes, very well.'

'The trouble is I sometimes think I am God.'

'You doubt it?'

'Most of the time.'

'And these doubts make you worry?'

'Oh yes.'

'We must remove the doubts one way or the other.'

'Yes please.'

'What powers do you have?'

The old man looked perturbed and paused a few seconds. 'Well, my friend Adam said that some water I gave him tasted like wine, so I suppose I must have changed it into wine.'

'Anything else?'

'No, not really. Oh, I was forgetting. A few weeks ago I said it was going to rain and it did. I've never had that before. I think I must have made it rain.'

'And that's all?'

'Yes.' The old man looked meekly down at the desk.

'Well listen, Herr Diskau. The emperor has heard of your case, and he commands you categorically to give up your claim to divinity. He says that there is no other god than the one he worships, and that your claim is sacrilegious and puts your soul in jeopardy. I have a certificate I will give you, signed and sealed by the emperor himself to the effect that you are not God. You must put this up on the wall of your living room. Do you understand?'

'Oh well, if the emperor says so,' the old man said sadly.

'You are not God.'

'Well, I just wondered.'

The old man was escorted out, and the consultant took notes. While he was writing another man was brought in. This man was very different. He was in his prime. He was several inches over six feet and very muscular. His features were strong, he had deep-set eyes with large dark eyebrows, and his chin protruded as did his lower lip. His hair was close cropped. He strode to the desk and sat down without invitation. He sat in silence while the consultant finished writing.

'How many alienists does it take to change a corset?' he was asked.

He made no answer.

'One, but the corset has got to really change.'

He sat, grim and motionless.

'Mmmm,' murmured the consultant. 'What is your name please?'

'My name is God,' said the client in a reverberating voice.

'Are you the God of the Old Testament or the New?'

'The Old.'

'So I am right in saying that you are vengeful, jealous, self-centred and that you create evil?'

'Evil…,' the client mused.

'Isaiah chapter forty five verse seven. "I create darkness and I create light. I create peace and I create evil. I am the Lord who does all these things." You said this?'

'Yes I create evil. I punish those who deserve it, I am helping them. You call me self-centred. It is only fitting that mortals should worship and serve me.'

'Do you ever doubt your divinity?'

'Not at all.'

'When did your apotheosis take place?'

'I have always been God.'

'And you have been confined to an asylum since you were fifteen?'

'That is true.'

'You created the world?'

'I did. Everything in the world belongs to me.'

'And you got into trouble through that belief?'

'I did. I was arrested on numerous occasions.'

'What is your view on Evil?'

'It is necessary that mankind should suffer Evil. It teaches them my divinity more effectively than goodness.'

'How so?'

'People take goodness for granted. It is only when they have a good piece of Evil that they sit up and think.'

'You would personally spread Evil?'

'I would.'

'Well, you may be God, but in your present state you are too dangerous to be let out of the asylum. The Old Testament God is not socially acceptable. Apart from that, the emperor says there is another God.'

'No! It's impossible!' The client pounded on the table and his face went red with rage.

'The emperor says so.'

'The emperor?'

'Yes. The emperor worships the God of the New Testament.'

'He ought to worship me.'

'If you want him to worship you, you must change. I will give you a pamphlet on the attributes of the Christian God. I want you to go away and copy them out five thousand times. "God is merciful. God is compassionate, etcetera." Come back in three weeks' time and I will talk to you again. I advise you to read the New Testament. You do want the emperor to worship you?'

'Yes I do.'

'Well, God can change. It is obvious from the Bible that God became more sympathetic at the time he caused a son to be born to him. Parenthood often makes men less harsh. What you have done is to revert to your old self. You might therefore consider reincarnating the Messiah. It would help. If you do as I say, you may in time be released from the asylum. You would like that?'

'I would.'

'Then you must do as I say. Humankind would like you better, and probably worship you more.'

'I will consider your request.'

'Good.'

With a frown on his forehead, the client rose from his chair and left the room to rejoin the coach and horses.

The next client ambled into the room accompanied by one of the costumed servants. He was short and plump, and had a large bushy beard. His hair was a tangle of many ringlets.

'My word, you look just like God!' exclaimed the consultant.

'I am God,' said the client, beaming amiably.

'Please take a seat.' God sat down. 'Your name please?'

'God.'

'I see, and what are your attributes?'

'Mercy, compassion, loving and others.'

'Good. Very good.'

God beamed.

'And what powers do you have?'

'I created the universe.'

'Good.'

'And I make butterflies fly round in circles.'

'Capital.'

'I can make flowers bloom.'

'Yes.'

'And make goats copulate.'

'Yes, yes. Go on.'

'I know all the secrets of men's hearts.'

'What an amazing mind you must have.'

'Indeed.'

'And do you ever doubt your powers?'

'I do sometimes.'

What effect does that have on you?

'It makes me very depressed.'

'And this depression lasts a long time?'

'A month or two usually.'

'I see. Well, let me consider.' The consultant intertwined his hands and rested his elbows on the desk. After a few seconds he spoke.

'All knowledge rests on faith, and it is natural that even – perhaps especially – you, with so much dependent on you, should doubt or shy away from your responsibilities. This is what your doubt is, a reflection of the seriousness with which you approach your task. If you do become depressed you must bear that in mind. If other people, by their attitudes, encourage doubt in you, you must take no notice; you cannot expect a great deal from mortals. I know them. But there is no need to doubt. You are God! You need have no doubts at all about that. Will you kindly put on the robes over there, and equip yourself with the sceptre and orb.'

God did as he was asked, and stood, beaming, tremendously happy. The consultant left his chair and knelt in front of God.

'Oh Lord who gives us life and nourishment, who watches over us with love and extends to us his care, we offer you our thanks and praise. We will never cease praising you, Lord. How can we when your greatness is so manifest?...' The consultant continued in this vein for quarter of an hour, after which he stood up and regained his seat. 'Are you happy now?' he asked.

'I have never been so happy,' said God.

'If you are ever unhappy or depressed, come here again. Now, I have a few more words to say to you. What God and his son Jesus are renowned for are being and doing good. If you wish people to worship you, you will have more success through helping people, for instance by digging their gardens, doing errands for them and so on.'

'Oh, I thought people had to do things for me.'

'No, no, no. What I say is written in the Bible. If you help other people, other people will do things for you. However, I would advise you against trying to heal people. If they have faith they will get better, and if not, worse. In fact if people get better then you can take it as a sign of their faith in you.'

'I suppose I must help other people, then.'

'Yes, you must.'

'Then so I will.'

'Excellent. I will write a note ordering your release from the asylum in a week's time. In the meantime I will call your relatives in, and some of the more prominent villagers and instruct them in how they must treat you and worship you. Please allow me to keep your regalia here in this room for safekeeping; it will be stolen otherwise. May I wish you joy in your new life.'

24/5/86

A NEW TREATMENT FOR PAIN

Dieter Aschenbach was a doctor of a philosophical turn of mind. He considered human experience in categories such as 'Thisness', 'Isness' and others more esoteric, and because of his medical concerns the problems of pain gave him much food for thought.

He had a patient who had been in continuous and practically unbearable pain since his fifteenth birthday, which had fallen on the first day of Ramadan. This suggested to the doctor that the pain might have been psychosomatic, not withstanding the professed atheism of the patient, but nothing anyone could do, with this insight, was to any effect. The most advanced painkillers at his disposal were equally of no help. What was the doctor to do?

The answer, after a little thought and dreaming, came to him. I will spare you the many ramifications of the proof of his fundamental tenet. His principle was that the dislike of pain was relative to the like of pleasure; one could not like pleasure if one had not experienced pain, and equally one could not dislike pain if one had not experienced pleasure. He made a separation, perhaps a little risky, between mental and physical pain, and proceeded on that basis.

A renowned hypnotist was summoned to the hospital and given instructions. He commenced by the means of a preamble which included the instructions to walk down a set of stairs, and subsequently to follow the progress of a yacht across an azure sea. Much to the doctor's relief, the patient proved an amenable subject, and passed into a deep trance. In this state the patient was immune to pain. Then, the doctor acted.

He possessed a sophisticated device for measuring pain and detecting it. The pain was located between the armpit and hip of the patient's right-hand side. Using a cunning device which encapsulated the entire body, while, however, allowing movement, the doctor was able to increase the pain, and spread the pain with exact evenness all over the body. It was important that the pain would be undeviatingly constant, and various 'safety' devices were connected to the device to ensure this end. In this state the patient would have no awareness of physical pleasure in relation to which he could know, and therefore dislike, the pain. The hypnotist was then asked to remove all memory of physical pleasure, as an additional safeguard, which he did.

The patient was brought out of his trance, and as he opened his eyes and regained normal consciousness, a broad and serene smile appeared on his face. The doctor questioned him about his condition, whether he felt pain, but the patient was merely puzzled by this attention. The hypnotist was dismissed, and the procedure was brought to an end by the administration of two kinds of tablet. One of these was a certain kind of tranquilliser which had the property of preventing dreams. This was in order that the patient might not experience physical pleasure in his dreams. The other, with a similar end in view, was to depress sexual feelings.

The patient, of necessity, was confined to the hospital for the rest of his life, but although he felt frustrated sometimes, in a need for greater physical movement, he was on the whole quite happy. The fame of Dieter Aschenbach spread far and wide.

29/5/86

A CHANCE MEETING

arold staggered out of the pub as he did every Monday night and to a lesser extent of stagger on the other days. Human beings were good. He would call out: 'You're beautiful,' to the women he passed, young or old, maybe give them a hug. It is possible. He would like to be in bed with a girl tonight. It would be gorgeous, or she would be.

Halfway home and he'd passed no-one on the street. It was always the same. But, then just ahead of him on a bench he saw someone sitting. Was it a woman? Maybe it was. It was. He stopped in front of her. On the bench was a figure dressed in torn and dirty trousers, a jacket with blue patches on, and a hat set at a jaunty angle with a jewel on it. She was thin.

'C'mon love, come home with me,' Harold belched hopefully.

'I've seen worse,' she said, smiling at him.

'Just because I've had a tipple or two. No come on, wouldn't you like me to hold you in my great strong arms?'

The woman laughed. 'I've got a few things to do first. You go home and I'll come on later,' she said.

'You liar.'

The woman laughed.

'How would you know where I lived anyway?' he demanded.

'I'll be there – well, probably.'

'Go on, give us a squeeze.'

'I don't mean like that.'

'Gawd, you've got short hair, you might be a bloke. Look, I'm really sorry, I've just had a bit to drink, y'know.'

The person laughed.

'Are you a woman, then?'

'Sometimes I think I'm a woman but sometimes I think I'm a man. I think I'm more woman than man.'

'What's all this then, you're not one of those people who's a man and a woman at the same time, bisexual hermaphrodite, is that it then?'

'Fraid so.'

'Bisexual hermaphrodite?'

'The lot,' she laughed

'You are a one. Trust my luck, but I bet you'd be alright in bed. No, hang on you might have Aids…'

'I have got Aids,' she said lightly.

Harold was struck dumb for a moment, then muttered, 'Oh you poor love.'

'Don't worry, you won't catch it from me.'

'Don't kid me.'

'Don't want me to come back with you now?' she said, smiling.

Harold frowned and lurched unsteadily. 'You're just trying to put me off. I know your game…' he said, wagging a finger at her.

'I never put anyone off.'

'…and you're black.'

'I'm a mix, quite a lot black, but I'm not sure who my parents were.'

'A black bastard!' Harold roared with laughter.

When he quietened down she answered him, 'So what if I'm black?'

'Well er…black women can be really beautiful.'

'I won't come back to you if you talk like that.'

'Look love, you sound bloody mixed up, you need me more than I need you.'

'I wouldn't be too sure.'

'Anyway, where do you come from?'

'I told you I don't know who my parents were, so how would I know where I'm from? I've been through children's homes, mental hospital, prison, war, you name it… I've been on drugs…'

'I feel sorry for you, love.'

'I feel sorry for you too.'

Harold's expression darkened. 'Now look, love, you've been having me on quite a lot. Just because I'm drunk it doesn't mean I'm gullible. All that shit about who you are just doesn't hold water. You talk straight to me and I'll talk straight to you. You need a place for the night and that's a fact. I can see it by the clothes you're wearing.'

'Sometimes I'm very rich.'

'Then why do you wear those clothes?'

'Rich people need me less.'

'I got it at last, you're a whore, that's it, isn't it? I bet you don't get far in that get up…'

The woman laughed. 'I do alright, I haven't died yet, but you might be wrong. You didn't even know whether I was a woman or not.'

'Alright, what do you do?'

'Same as a lot of people.'

'Out on the streets.'

'Sometimes, but I stay in a lot of places; I know loads of people.'

'Do you believe in free love then?'

'That's part of it but not quite like you mean it.'

'I think you're a really interesting woman.'

'I bet you do.'

'Yeah, well…. Drunk strange man asking loads of questions. Why don't you just tell me to piss off?'

'I never tell people that, even quite unpleasant ones.'

'That's going a bit far. I mean you're alright with me, but you could get into serious trouble…'

'I've been lucky so far, but I'm a trusting person. You can get a long way with trust. The trouble's the other way round, people keep leaving me, and I can get people into bad trouble, you know.'

'How many you had, then?'

'Millions,' she said laughing.

'Go on, you haven't had one, have you?'

'You'd be surprised if you knew the truth.'

Harold laughed appreciatively. 'Well, whatever you are you seem quite happy,' he said.

'That's partly because you're talking to me, but you're right, I'm often quite happy.'

'Where'd you get that jewel?'

'I'm not sure.'

'You could flog it if you're hard up.'

'No, I'd never sell it, it's part of me, I'm very rich really.'

'Well…' Harold paused, looking sad.

'Yes, you must be going, but I'll come on later.'

'Like hell you will,' grumbled Harold.

The woman smiled.

'What's your name in case I ever see you again?' he said.

'Guess. It's an old-fashioned name.'

'Gloria.'

'No.'

'Beryl?'
'No.'
'Victoria?'
'Warmer.'
'Salome then, for Gawd's sake.'
There was a pause, and the two looked at each other.
'My name is Hope,' she said.

13/11/1986

THE FUGITIVE

The foreign power had occupied the country. Phillipe sat in his house reading a book. There was a frenzied knocking at the door. Phillipe answered it. 'I need...' The intense whisper of the stranger was cut short by Phillipe.

'Are you looking for the way through the wasteland at the back of these houses, or is it me you want to see? Say "the first" or "the second".'

'The second,' the stranger said, too much in a rush to question.

'Come in and say nothing.'

The stranger hurried in and made toward the stairs.

'Perhaps you are tired after your journey. However, it is pointless to go upstairs now as you will not sleep later. Then it is almost certain that you would be disturbed if I were to have another visitor, and I have an idea that I might have one. Do you understand? Think carefully.... Sit down, and I will bring you some coffee.'

Phillipe walked into the kitchen area and prepared cheap coffee. The stranger took a seat and started to speak.

'My name...'

'Quiet! In my house visitors speak only when they are spoken to, at least to begin with. Do you understand?' Phillipe came back with the coffee. He laughed. 'I know it seems silly, it's like the old fashioned attitude to children, and I am only thirty! Still it is important to us, or rather to me.' Phillipe looked into the stranger's eyes. He took a seat opposite the occupied chair. 'Have you heard of the play by Oscar Wilde, "The Importance Of Being Earnest"?' he asked.

'Look, I didn't come here to discuss literature with you,' the stranger snapped.

'Please be quiet and listen. Perhaps I am an egotist, an egoist. At times I need an audience, and as I am offering you my hospitality it is for you to listen. It is a curious if trivial story. Two of the characters in it have more than one name. Jack is Jack in the country and Ernest in the town. Likewise, Algernon visits an invalid and wholly fictitious friend called Bunbury who serves as an excuse for various pleasurable escapades. The practice is called "Bunburying".' Phillipe went on to give other details of the plot and quotations from the play. 'What is your name now? If anyone calls looking for you I will say that I have someone of the name you now give me staying.'

The stranger looked at Phillipe, puzzled, but intrigued. He gave the question a moment's thought.

'My name is Raymond Bailey,' he replied.

'I am Phillipe. And how old are you?'

'Twenty-eight.'

'Good. I'm glad you're twenty-eight, we will get on well.'

'It doesn't always follow.'

'In this case it does.'

There was a silence. Phillipe lit a cigarette and continued.

'I have a terrible memory. If someone came and asked me today I would tell them that you arrived today, but in a week's time I might say that you'd been here a week and a half, in a month, a month and a half. For instance I have no idea what day or date it is today.'

'It's…'

Phillipe held up his hand. 'I don't work, you see, and there is no need to tell me – all the days are the same, even for shopping. The corner shops are open on Sundays.'

'What makes you think I want to stay?' asked Raymond.

'Well, don't you?'

'Yes, but how do you know?'

'I often put up people who are homeless and/or mentally disturbed, perhaps they've been in hospital. They try me for refuge or help. If you're not homeless and mentally disturbed I won't put you up here. Are you mentally disturbed?'

Raymond hesitated. 'Yes, I have been in mental hospital.'

'Have a cigarette, I think you should smoke, it's very therapeutic.'

'No thanks.'

'Do you take drugs of any kind, medicinal ones for instance?'

'No.'

'Why?'

'I wouldn't agree to take them.'

'Very wise. Incidentally, you were sent here by someone, weren't you?'

'Yes. It was…'

'Oh, that doesn't matter…'

'It was…'

'Be quiet – if you tell me I will throw you out.'

'Why?'

'I have my quirks. Now what exactly is your disturbance? Is it schizo-phrenia of some kind, a persecution complex for instance?'

'It's not schiz…'

'You think that "they" are trying to kill you? Or something less than that?'

'They will kill me.'

'That is serious; however, you will be ready to face the world in a little time. You may not feel that the time is right, but I will know better than you, I do have some experience. I know that it is difficult for someone in your state to be so self-controlled, but there are certain things you must not talk about or else I will throw you out. You will soon learn what these are.'

'Such as what?'

'I think it is counterproductive to talk about the past. Either you are merely clinging to the causes of your illness and through them, the illness itself, or you are comparing your present state to a more idyllic former state, to the detriment of the present, thus compounding your sense of ill-ness. I work rather by a side step than a head on clash. Just as finding the right environment can make life much better for such a person as you, so can finding the right mental environment – to put the illness in a cottage by the sea, metaphorically speaking. When you leave here, it will be more likely that you will find both cottages. People such as yourself usually lie indoors all the time, often with the curtains drawn, and don't do very much. This must change, but for the moment it is wise; to go outside will only fuel your fears of persecution. If I find you have gone outside at all, then your being here will have been useless. I will throw you out. How-ever, I will drive you to do certain tasks such as keeping yourself clean, cooking and washing up. If you do not, again I will throw you out.'

'It is only because I am desperate that I will stay here,' said Raymond.

'You stay here to make a break with the past. You will later find your stay here to have been useful.'

'You are sure of that? How can you be sure?'

'I know. Trust me. You will be a new man. As we go along, I will sug-gest changes you can make. To start with I will get you some new clothes from a charity shop, you will give me your measurements and I will burn your old clothes. You will grow a beard, you will feel emotionally less vulnerable. When I say you will, you realise what the consequences of refusal mean?'

Raymond nodded.

'Now let's talk about something else. What would you like for supper, for instance?'

The two carried on a relaxed conversation while Phillipe prepared the supper. Phillipe promised to teach Raymond how to cook; institutions didn't teach anyone how to cook. After supper, Phillipe put on a coat and put the radio in a bag. Raymond's reaction was a worried one. 'Where are you going?' he demanded.

'Trust me, it is in your interests.'

'Why are you taking the radio? I need to listen to it.'

'All that's on these days are propaganda programmes, lists of names, and descriptions of wanted persons, and that awful military music all the time. It will be too disturbing to you, and I am getting fed up with it. It will be a present for a friend.'

'Can't I have a newspaper?'

'I will get you a children's comic, that will be far more suitable, besides which I have books.'

At another house in the town, Phillipe handed over the radio to his friend Gwendolen.

'I don't want you to come to my house any more,' he said.

'Oh! What's this, the pay-off then, you...?'

'I will come to you.'

'Well that's not so bad, but why are you doing this, the radio, the change of "policy"? You're so arbitrary.'

'I can't help being arbitrary, Gwendolen. Accept it, you know you've got my affection.'

Life continued in a fairly relaxed way for several days. One evening, Phillipe proposed a new pastime.

'Well, we've talked about philosophy, religion, foreign languages, and you're obviously quite bright. Did you take a qualification of some kind?'

'I am an engineer.'

'You mean before your breakdown you were an engineer?'

'Er, yes. Yes, of course.'

'Listen carefully. I was a Biochemistry student twelve years ago, from

1997 to 2000. I would like to teach you everything I know. No! Don't worry. I have forgotten most of it. Being, as I have said, an egotist, I want also to tell you about myself – a great deal. You will then be able to know what it is like to be me.'

Raymond nodded and scratched the shallow stubble on his cheeks.

'You must pay great attention,' said Phillipe.

'OK,' said Raymond.

The house was small and had only one bedroom. Phillipe slept upstairs in the bedroom, and Raymond in the living room on an airbed. Phillipe, generally, was awake till late in the following day. There were often noises outside, and by some physical peculiarity of the house and area, night noises could be heard as clearly in the bedroom of Phillipe as out in the street. One night, at three in the morning, Phillipe heard Raymond speaking, and, listening more carefully, the sounds of a voice answering on the telephone. He listened intently. In the darkness, if it could have been seen, first a worried expression crossed Phillipe's face, but then a smile, which remained for some time.

For the next two months life continued smoothly, punctuated by phone calls, intercepted in a sense by Phillipe. By the end of this time Raymond had an apparently long-established growth of beard, and it had become time for the next conversation of any significance.

'Well Raymond, it's almost time for you to go now. How do you feel?'

'It's not time yet. Where do I go?' protested Raymond.

'It will be easy for you, but you must listen carefully to what I say. I have wanted you to know how it was to be me, but there are a few other material articles of knowledge. Here are my birth certificate, my cheque book, card, and library card. These are important to my identity too. If I were to go away anywhere I would take them with me. If I were to lose my identification papers and number, these would get me out of trouble, and I'd get new ones. On the other hand, if I were to lose them I would still have my identification papers together with my signature for the bank, and my memory of birthplace and date.' Phillipe put the documents back in the drawer. 'These are very important to me, you understand? What if I were to lose them? I would go to the bank and cancel my cheques and so on, then to the library, then since I had identification papers I would probably never know I'd lost my birth certificate. If for instance someone like you were to steal my cheque book, I wouldn't go to the police; people such as you cannot help yourselves.'

The talk meandered on till late at night. Phillipe drew it to a close by telling Raymond that he must leave by dawn to avoid a sentimental parting, expressing sympathy for the difficulty he would face, and good wishes. They retired to bed.

The next morning, Phillipe came downstairs at nine o'clock. Raymond stood waiting for him by the desk. On the desk were the birth certificate, cheque book and various cards.

'Hello Raymond. Why haven't you gone?'

'My name is not Raymond, it is Alan Makepeace. I work for the state subversion department of the military. My task has been to try and make it too risky for anyone to hide a member of the resistance, by spreading the fear that he or she might be one of us. I have hung on to the end, but I have lost with you, there is nothing you have said on which a conviction could be brought. I have checked up on your friends through your address book. Many of them have indeed been in mental hospital, and been put up by you. There is however one prosecution we can make, and that is of your friend who said I might find "refuge" here. Unfortunately, as he did not hide me, but merely directed me, he cannot be put to death, only sent to a prison camp with hard labour. I will deal with it now so that you have no chance to warn him.'

He phoned through to headquarters and a team of men were sent around to arrest Phillipe's friend. Phillipe and he sat in silence for an hour until the phone rang.

'For me.' Alan answered it. After a few seconds he slammed the phone down and turned on Phillipe, glowering. 'He has gone! They broke down the door, and everything has gone!' Alan strode up and down the room, then stopped, staring at Phillipe. 'For three months I've listened to your blasted prattle. I've grown a beard like a caveman, and I've had to wear clothes of fifty years ago. I've had to wash up for you, cook meals, I haven't seen daylight for three months. Blast you! Now I am going, and I hope I never see you again.'

Alan marched out of the door, slamming it behind him. Phillipe sank into his favourite chair and chuckled. It would be sad if his friend were caught, but that was unlikely; he would be far away by now. If he did get caught, his warning to escape would have come through an anonymous message.

27/06/1986.

REFLECTIONS OF A LITERARY MAN ON
THE EATING OF A CAKE

any miles away in the market town of X was a coffee shop. I happened to be in this coffee shop. The interior of the place was half timbered, the woodwork interspersed with white wall, and here and there a bay window. The tables were of dark and scuffed oak, the chairs plushly upholstered. Outside, murders may have been committed, but not here. Here only the calm conspiracy – of what to do next in the process of shopping.

An old lady came through the door and wove through the shop to a particular – and I would think, in her mind – prearranged table. She seemed quite certain of where she was going. She wore a nondescript coat which covered up her oblong and muscular build. Her face protruded from her coat, and at a glance I could see the look of determination on her oblong face. Her grey hair was slicked back over her head, possibly to hide a touch of baldness. At length a waitress came to her and asked for her order. She pointed to the trolley, presumably to one particular cake-bedded area on it, and said firmly, 'One of those.' I liked her nonchalance.

Many authors have subjected food to scrutiny, such as Boeuf Bourguinon (or alternatively fish and chips). But where, outside a children's story, is a cake mentioned? The reason is that eating a cake is both a childish and undignified thing to do, and when it is undertaken by a grown up, a ritual is needed to disguise the fact. Future readers may credit me with a small degree of genius for publicising this forbidden corner.

If this was her weekly or monthly treat, no sign of recognition was given when the cake, having been found, was delivered. 'Thank you,' was all she said. I admired her for this economy and refinement.

The cake itself was a lusty and turgid creation of great lusciousness. Irresistibly and ruthlessly she began (after a slight pause) to consume the cake.

To continue where I left off. In the literature of ancient Greece and

Rome, are cakes mentioned? Indeed not, their peoples are too busy fighting wars. What would Virgil have said? I feel sure that he would have regarded cake eating as quite decadent or at least misguided. And the feeling lingers on; the most exuberant cakes are only eaten in secrecy of a sort.

Although from my distance it was hard to disentangle the expression and play of inner working on the lady's face, I detected great concentration there. She ate very slowly with a fork; she had great control, hoping, I think, not to betray her excitement.

'Alright, Miss Y?' she was asked.

'I'll manage,' I think she said, taking me into the secret of the magnitude of her task.

I meditated on the spectacle with interest. Firstly I considered which of the various categories of teeth might be responsible in what I now witnessed. But I realised with a jolt of enlightenment that with such a cake and such a person, the eating was not done with the teeth, or indeed even with the tongue. I realised that there are not sufficient words in our vocabulary to describe the internal labour of eating such a cake. Devouring for instance refers only to the franticness of the act of eating. We have 'chewing' but this really refers to gum or blubber. 'Mulching' to me sounds more accurate. However…

She was totally engrossed. Her movements were uniform so far as I could tell, apart of course from the manoeuvring of the fork in a subtly different way each time to pursue the retreating cake. How could she bear its coquetry? It flirted with her; the eyelashes of its dimples fluttered encouragingly, teasingly. And all this was taken in and considered with a great deal of skill and experience, I feel sure. No way could that cake get around her. Although at one point, as I watched, I thought I saw her eyes dart to the cake trolley. Surely she couldn't have been considering…? Words fail me. The cake had almost won the contest.

Her victory, though, was inevitable, and the cake suffered the fulfilment of its destiny. Birth, life and death may follow each other in a great cycle, but for that cake, I suspect, there was something final, perhaps in cake terms a Nirvana.

The old lady, having done so much for the cake, laid her fork noisily on the plate. I thought I detected a smile on her face. If this was in fact so, I can well understand it. Earlier in my life I have a memory of eating a similar confection, and being asked on completion how I felt. 'Happy,' I said.

There were a few minutes silence and immobility, after which reality broke in, in the guise of a waitress with a bill. I felt sad that the dirty business of a monetary transaction should sully the occasion. Was it not a kind of prostitution? However, the old lady seemed content, or at least showed no sign of resentment. The transaction having been completed, she said a word of farewell to the waitress and anonymously left the shop.

In life there are many great risks and disappointments that stand in the way of achieving our heart's desire. What if all the tables had been full, for instance? Think of the minor ruffling there would have been had the waitress this time have been the new one. What if, having planned the day's outing, she'd received a bill for a library fine in the morning? What if, instead of that particular cake there had only been a piece of Battenburg?

Well…

28/02/1987

GIVING

'm dying,' Matilda said gently.

'Would you like a cup of tea?' Tulip her daughter asked briskly.

Matilda laughed good-humouredly.

'What on earth are you laughing at? I asked you if you wanted some tea, there's nothing funny about that,' Tulip snapped.

'Oh well, I suppose it keeps me from self pity,' Matilda said, laughing a little more.

'Do you want a cup of tea?' Tulip said firmly.

'Yes child, bring me some tea,' Matilda said, sighing.

Tulip half turned from her mother's bedside but then turned back and confronted her. 'You called me child. How dare you call me child. It's ridiculous, I'm fifty-three now, and I don't want to hear any nonsense about how I'm always your child…'

'You are a child, Tulip.'

'Well if I am a child, you made me that way…'

'Quiet now, Tulip, please. I do have something to do with how you are, but you will never understand what else is involved too…'

'And you called me such a stupid name…'

'I had hopes of you.'

'Never call me your "child" again. Besides, do you really think I want people to think I am your daughter?'

'No Tulip, I won't call you child again,' Matilda sighed.

Tulip frowned and hurriedly left the room. In the kitchen she wandered around working off her annoyance. She forgot all about the tea she had been going to make for her mother and sat down at the kitchen table.

Out of the blankness of her mind, almost unconsciously, a word from her mother's speech came back – 'dying'. She'd lived up till now, why should she die? People did that sometimes, it was possible. Tulip looked around herself. What if she *was* going die? She relapsed into blankness for a while, then looked around herself with greater interest. If her mother was going to die, all this would be hers, now that was quite a thought. But would she die soon? Tulip couldn't wait forever. She'd better check. She walked back into her mother's bedroom. Matilda laughed when she saw her daughter coming.

'What are you laughing at?' Tulip demanded, frowning.

'You've forgotten something,' her mother said with a hint of mischief around her eyes and lips.

Tulip frowned even more.

'Mother,' she said, 'how do you know you're dying?'

'One knows these things.'

'How?'

'I know. You will know too one day.'

'Do you want to me fetch a doctor?'

'Doctors, at least at this time in history, cannot provide immortality.'

Tulip stood silently, looking at her mother.

'Look Tulip, look out of the window. See the wind.'

Tulip looked out on the swaying trees and bushes, the driven leaves. 'How can you see the wind, it's nothing but air?'

'I see everything,' her mother said with a smile.

'That's pretentious and impossible.'

'Perhaps a bit,' Matilda sighed.

'How can you see everything?'

'Well, I can see quite a lot. Close your eyes, Tulip. Yes! Don't look puzzled, close your eyes. Good. Now try and see a cube. No, I'm not playing games, this is serious. Do you see a cube?'

'No, I can see a bit of a square, then it goes away.'

'Try and turn the square over so that you can see three faces of the cube.'

'I can't see a thing now. What are you getting at?'

'Tulip, I can see a cube from all six sides at once…'

'That's nonsense, how can you?'

'I assure you, it can be done.'

'So…?'

'So I can see a lot. Now go and make that cup of tea please.'

Tulip walked into the kitchen, forgetting the cup of tea as she went. Dying – it had never happened before. Her father had eloped with another woman when she was young. All artists were a bit like that, she supposed. At least her mother had not sent her away from home. Artists did that as well, She'd once read a book about one, that was when she'd been interested in reading, she wasn't now. True, her mother had hinted that it might be better for her to go, but she'd never actually said 'go.' Now she wouldn't go, ever. Or would she? If her mother actually did die, might it not be better for her to rid herself of her mother's ghost? Move somewhere else? That was another thing that had never happened before. Perhaps a smaller house, and have some money left over. She could travel. Three things. No, her mother wasn't so bad as all that. That was a fourth thing. Careful, Tulip.

Days and a few weeks passed by until one day, coming down the stairs, she heard the sound of crying coming from her mother's room. The crying sounded ugly, and she wondered whether to do anything about it. She'd never heard her mother cry before. Irresistibly, some force within her drove her into her mother's room. By the bed she stopped and said, 'Stop crying mother. What is it?'

The crying continued, she couldn't bear it. She repeated the question several times, each time more insistently, a little more desperately. There was no change. She looked at her mother's face with tears creeping down it, at a loss. Impetuously she bent down, took Matilda in her arms and kissed her clumsily on the forehead. The tears streamed on a little, but the noise stopped.

'Give me my hanky, Tulip, please.'

Tulip released her mother and gave her the handkerchief. Her mother dried her face, blew her nose then lay down again. Smiling faintly, she looked into Tulip's eyes. Tulip blushed. 'Are you better now?' she asked mechanically.

'Tulip…You have the power to make people happy.' She stopped and coughed. 'Including yourself.'

Tulip stayed silent.

'You've never thought much about happiness, have you?'

Tulip's face was motionless.

'When you loved me…'

'Loved?'

'Yes, when you loved me just now, you loved…well, never mind. However, I didn't cry to make that happen. Please Tulip, get me a drink and let's have a chat. Please now, there's a good…please,' Matilda smiled. 'A strong drink!' she shouted as best she could after the disappearing bulk of Tulip.

Tulip came back with some sherry that hadn't been touched for years. 'Tulip, I want to have an exhibition. It depends on you. There may be some difficulty, but I think you can get over it. That's why I was crying, I didn't think I could do, but since you kissed me I think maybe I can. Tulip! It's one last time before I die. I want to make a splash. I'll get the "art loving public" to give me a good send off, there's no-one else that will…'

'But you haven't painted for years.'

'I have, only you've never noticed – secretly, in bed here. They're my best. Look! There's one below the window there in brown paper. There are others in the cupboard over there. Now will you do it? Please! One last thing for me. I've never asked much of you, but please – just this once?'

Tulip looked bewildered.

'Don't say no, Tulip, I beg you.'

Tulip blushed. 'Yes mother, I'll try,' she said.

'Tulip, I love you,' her mother said.

They discussed the details.

The next day Tulip went into town to the little picture gallery her mother had mentioned.

'Is this person a professional artist?' she was asked.

'Yes, she is.'

'Well, we always consider the work of serious artists.'

'How much will it cost?'

'I prefer to discuss matters like that when we have agreed on exhibiting.'

'Money is no object. Big money,' said Tulip.

'I'm sorry but it's as I said.'

'How soon could she have an exhibition?'

'We're booked up for the next three years.'

'No, that's too long,' Tulip said worriedly.

'But we'll certainly consider her.'

Tulip walked awkwardly to the door, and as she was half out of it she said bitterly, 'What if the artist is dead by then?'

The other gallery in town was booked up. Over the next weeks she went to galleries further and further afield, and the more refusals she got the more desperate and determined she became. The word 'now' was used in each gallery. At the end of this time she was asked by a gallery manager, 'And what is the name of the artist in question?'

'Matilda Hastings,' she replied.

'Matilda Hastings! Oh yes! It's ages since anyone has seen her work.'

'You know her?' asked Tulip, surprised.

'Know of her, yes, and we certainly want her.' Tulip told him her story. 'We'll reschedule our exhibition if it's as close as all that. There'll be some difficulty, but I think it'll be understood.'

'Oh, thank you sir.'

The gallery manager laughed. Tulip blushed.

Tulip went home and told her mother the news. 'Well, I'll hold out until then, I think. The life urge is very strong, especially when there's something like this happening.'

Over the next few weeks there were phone calls and vans calling. The press were invited to the preview. It was all very professionally done, and Tulip herself had a lot to do with the organisation. She became quite excited about the exhibition; every day she went to her mother and discussed with her its progress. She went so far as to discuss with her mother the clothes she ought to wear when, as her representative, she'd declare the exhibition open. Her mother advised her not to say too much but to listen to what people had to say.

They had some very pleasing things to say, as it turned out, and the press were more than kind in their congratulations and criticism. Tulip felt proud of her mother and went almost every day to guard the gallery. As the exhibition continued her mother spoke less and less and took less food. It was when she heard that another picture had been sold that she spoke a few words and took a few sips of the sherry. She didn't tease Tulip anymore, except once when she said, 'Well Tulip, I'm going soon, and you'll have all those good things you've been thinking about.'

Tulip blushed and her mother laughed. She seemed contented, but something was missing and Tulip couldn't make out what it was.

One day when Tulip came downstairs and went into her mother's room to say goodbye she got no answer. She went to the bed and spoke louder but there was no response. She ran into the garden, frantically looking for a feather, just a small one. She'd seen this done on television once. She took the feather back and held it over her mother's nose. It fluttered. She breathed a sigh of relief. She shook her mother gently but mother didn't open her eyes. Slowly she sat down on the chair next to her mother's bed. She found her mother's left hand, withdrew it from the bed, and held it between her own. She watched her mother's face intently. A faint smile appeared on it. The smile didn't fade.

20/10/86

LOVE STORY

When I first saw Rachel and her daughter together I thought they were sisters. There is a gentle tragedy in these words.

We both worked at the same hall together as cleaners. I was there first, then Rachel came. Together, or separately, we polished floors, brass light switches, set fires, covered chairs for the evening function. The first thing that would be noticed about Rachel was her great beauty. I am convinced of it. Surely anyone would have seen this. It wasn't a contemporary beauty or of any period of this century or culture. I think it was an ancient Hebrew beauty, with her long black hair, her unaffected poise. Strangely, I don't remember noticing this at first. Perhaps I was above such things! But gradually we became friends, and I found that her beauty went further than that.

I had only very occasionally spoken to anyone for quite a long time. She wasn't a great one for words either. With her, I talked. We talked, and how we talked! And not just talk, laughter. I remember once a cat raced into the hall and to its far end, disappeared, then raced out again the same way, ignoring us, feet away. I remember the delighted laughter. I think we must have seemed like two children lost in a secret beautiful world. I have no idea what she thought about us; I try to tell myself that she was like that with all her friends.

The secret beautiful world began to extend for me beyond our conversations, and as I worked in another part of the big hall I felt so happy just to be in the same place. When I went home, she was there too. She was a strange mix, a heady brew. I think you would have found her burning with life, but at the same time so calm, never agitated. It seems to me now that she loved without knowing that she loved. At the time I hoped it was me that she loved, but I think now it went far wider, although I might have been included. She had the gift which I suppose Tibetan Lamas have of, without insincerity, making you feel that you are the most important: complete attention. This 'love' showed in everything about her but especially in her eyes. If you were fortunate or unfortunate enough to meet her eyes in a quiet place, what was there? The gentle smile on her face, but in her eyes! There was such an intensity. What was it? Love? No, passion of some kind. Rachel was an artist, a painter; I think what was in those eyes was genius.

I have heard someone say that there is a precise moment when nature reveals her spell. I caught her gaze in this way. I stepped backwards. She seemed so new and bright to me. How could she be troubled in any way? Yet in the little she spoke about herself I realised that her life and her life within had not been easy. There was a darkness there, and perhaps this was in her eyes too, but if it was, what was in her eyes was stronger than any darkness. I loved her more for this darkness.

Although she had seen more of life than I had, she had something that young children have, a knowledge of the irrelevance, or an unconsciousness of the barriers that divide people and peoples. She seemed unconscious of her beauty too; she was completely without vanity. Amongst her ancestors and family circle were many illustrious figures, but these were of no consequence either, and if she mentioned them at all there was no hint whatsoever of name-dropping. I was slightly in awe of these names, but I realised that to her they were much as relations or acquaintances of mine were to me. Besides, she had no need of names, she made her own life and struggle.

Something that young children have, I remember. I had to sleep in the hall to guard some merchandise. In the morning the merchant, Rachel, and I were together.

'Did you see the man with his head under his arm, Luke?' he asked.

'Oh yes, I did, I gave him a piece of toast.'

'You didn't!' Rachel gasped, open-mouthed.

We kept up the pretence, but later in the day I told her the truth, laughing.

'Well, I don't care if I *am* naive,' she said.

I loved her for that.

Naivety is something sneered at. Critical remarks are made about it, and in the wrong hands it is indeed very dangerous. Wars have been and may be fought because of it. But perhaps it was this 'naivety' which gave her strength and courage. If there was a wrong or an injustice, it was she who was far more effective at standing up against it. Also, if this was naivety, then before you think me patronising, I was inside this naivety myself, though not in quite the same way. It is my naivety to think that I might fulfil in life the visions I have given myself. I too am glad I am naïve.

I never knew her *very* well. Well enough to know her faults – for she must have had them – but if there was a fault, it was in my eyes the curious distance she had: she was both closer and more distant than anyone else I knew. Who could ever have hugged her? I felt, 'No, I must never touch her.' Well, I was younger then, not much, but enough to make a difference.

To be close yet very distant: a psychotherapist can do that. But that wasn't it. Analysis would be too arid or severe a word for any way of understanding that was hers. But her understanding was not at all flippant or superficial and she was very thorough. Most of the time she only showed by the odd word the depth of her thought. I think that her language must really have been visual. I remember once the remarkable slowness and thoroughness with which she had read a short story. She knew that short story in some ways better than its author. Only someone who intensely wants to understand but is out of their element in a different language can approach words in this way – this capacity for attention to or perhaps obsession with detail, but seeing each detail as something new. Perhaps to most this seems odd or even disturbed, but done in the right way it is miles above pedantry, above the poor imitators.

Yes! Indeed I was proud of her, and I had dreams for her, dreams from which I did my best, though not with great success, to exclude myself and let her be. I don't know quite what has become of her and her painting, but it somehow seems fitting that she would remain a secret amongst those who know her and her work; the glare of success seems too crude. Although, perhaps, that is one way I hope to keep her to myself. She was my discovery, a very special friend, and try as I might I couldn't think ordinary thoughts about her. Perhaps sometimes I likened her to a great wild black panther, wild but gentle. A friend of hers once asked me where she was.

'She's padding around somewhere upstairs,' I had said.

Oh! She was such a mystery to me! But I say this to you, I am apologising to you for what I felt, and I feel ashamed. I don't want to let go of what I felt then or what I can remember. It is an inspiration in the dark at times.

Towards the end of her stay at the hall Rachel became more sombre and withdrawn. I'd begged her not to go, but she was going. There must have been some kind of trouble in her life beyond the odd things she told me. We seemed to drift apart. I remember the last time I saw her at the hall; she'd come to pay her respects to the custodian. I stopped her as she left the office and tried a few words, but realised she didn't want to stop.

'Well, I can't keep you,' I said. She nodded.

I wonder whether that communication had the same meaning for her as it did for me. I went to stack some chairs. As I worked I saw out of the corner of my eye that she'd stopped in the passage outside the office, watching me. I carried on working. I don't think that she knew that I'd seen her. Why had she looked at me in such a way? I still think about that look.

Some time before she left she showed me her paintings. She has a photographic portfolio of her work. We sat in a café and went through it. The paintings were very dark but with great richness, like old masters, and in fact they were built up like old masters with many layers of paint and glazing. She talked a little. It was hard for her to talk, and she talked about them in such a way that it was like an attack or an act of defiance. I felt honoured to have been taken into her confidence. What was the darkness of her paintings? The darkness in herself or in the history of her tribe? There was one though that was different, a painting of three figures seated between pillars, or was it one figure centrally? A figure not dark but bright and alive.

In my imagination I see her working on this painting in her room amongst all the clutter of her enormous canvases. She paints herself as a young magical prince enthroned amongst her own fears and darkness. It may not be a male figure – probably it is of indeterminate sex. It may be that I remember the youngling as male, because I would have liked to have been this prince. She looks up, there is a break in her concentration, and for the first time today she notices the sunshine through the windows. Her eyes go back to the painting.

'Yes,' she thinks, 'I must work more on the central figure.'

24/02/1987

JUDAS

Judas was a compassionate man. He was different from the other disciples of Jesus, not especially in this respect, but in the respect of his background and education. Compared to the first disciples, who were fisherman, Judas was sophisticated, both in understanding and in his thoughts. His faith in Jesus was the greatest amongst the disciples, and even preceded acquaintance with him. Unlike most people, to whom the coming of the Messiah had been but a figure of speech learned by rote, occasionally passing into belief, Judas had *believed* from an early stage in his life, and devoted much time and precocious thought to his belief, pestering the priests for disclosure of obscure and now unavailable writings, which were destroyed by jealous priests at the time of Jesus' ministry. Many prophecies are alluded to in the gospels which cannot be found in the Bible. Consequently, when he was fifteen, he – perhaps only he (besides a few shepherds and Persian astrologers) – was aware of the birth of Christ, outside the family circle of Jesus' surrogate mother and honorary father. Apart from the wonder of Jesus himself, Judas was fired by an even greater wonder, known only by himself, and perhaps to a hermit in the desert, and this is what it was.

Men in history often sought for immortality. Gilgamesh of Uruk was one, or a reflection of this, as more recently have been Fu Manchu and the alchemists; probably the search still goes on for more material forms of it. Judas was in the ancient and persistent tradition, but unlike the others his quest was selfless: he sought immortality for all. The Jews spoke little of heaven, and when they did, the word was used to define the sky and the stars which studded it. Judas had studied the ancient writings, and the soul was known to him. It was his unique discovery to find that through a certain eventuality it would be possible for the souls of humankind to ascend to heaven and exist for eternity in a state of bliss. This was salvation indeed! Not the more down-to-earth salvation which was commonly spoken of by the Jews. In conjunction with other writings it implied to him that, until the time in history when this eventuality was made actual, all souls of the deceased existed asomatically in the region of our world, knowing neither happiness nor unhappiness. The state is now known to us as Limbo, although we have lost Judas's original word for it. This was not good enough for Judas; he sought the eternal bliss of humankind. The eventuality he discovered, and on which so much depended, was the premature death of the Christ. So, yet again, before he had met Jesus, he had chosen himself as the means of bringing this to pass.

His resolve was strong, but he was a sensitive man, and was filled with anguish for what he must do. To kill the son of God! To inflict suffering on one who was without equal amongst men, and for whom he had so much love. However, his inner disturbance was ameliorated during the time of his discipleship by the pleasure of service, and of hearing the gospel; this was important to humankind too. Just as Jesus knew the sins of those who would have stoned an adulteress to death, and wrote them in the sand, he knew the mind of Judas. Hence, Judas was not predestined to do what he did, but did it freely, and the foreknowledge of Jesus was based on what we would now call his clairvoyant powers. Free will being retained, morality, heaven and hell are saved from absurdity and injustice.

When Jesus said on meeting him, 'It is better that you had not been born,' he was being compassionate. He knew the anguish which Judas suffered, and probably would suffer, and the hatred with which future Christians would regard both him and the Jewish race. Having a physical body, Jesus knew that he himself would suffer pain, but nonetheless he knew the selflessness and goodness of Judas, and didn't hold his intention against him. It must be remembered that Judas as well as the other disciples was granted healing and other powers, and used them to good effect.

Throughout his ministry Jesus often had to contend with crowds and Pharisees who wanted to kill him, but managed to escape this death successfully by hiding, or by escaping to another district. Some said his claim of divinity was blasphemous. Others, acknowledging the many miracles he performed, said that he was a devil come to lead them astray. The multitudes of men and women who followed him grew all the time, however, and the chief priests were forced to admit that, in time, all people would follow him. So it is possible that, eventually, his existence in this world could have become secure. Jesus avoided this death, certainly not out of cowardice, but for two reasons. Firstly, in order that the message should be heard as entirely and widely amongst the Jews as possible, and, secondly, in order to bestow the privilege of killing him on Judas, a killing motivated by love and selflessness, rather than hatred. Those that killed through hatred, he reasoned, would be destined for eternal damnation.

The duration of Judas's discipleship seemed long to him, through its beauty, but especially through the secret he carried with him. He had to use his judgement as to when the teaching would be complete, and it would therefore be time to bring about the death of Jesus. The more he thought about it, the more worry he felt about carrying out the act himself. He needed help. He went to the palace of Caiphas the high priest, and sought audience with him. Caiphas, on hearing that a disciple of Jesus had come to him, was most curious, and willingly set aside time for Judas.

Firstly Judas tried to convince Caiphas of the Christ. 'Esias prophesied that "A virgin shall conceive and that her son shall be the son of God".'

'And you believe that this has happened?'

'On the testimony of his earthly parents and of some shepherds who were visited by an angel shortly before his birth.'

Judas went on to demonstrate the fulfilment of many prophecies, and to name witnesses for miracles which had taken place. Caiphas proved an open and enlightened man, who had himself almost accepted the divinity of Jesus; he wasn't hard to talk with. Judas quoted to him the writings which showed the consequences of Christ's death. The prophecies of Isaiah which relate to the death of a man 'who was cut off out of the land of the living, for the transgression of my people was he stricken' were tacitly understood by the two men not to refer to the Christ.

'Well, I am not quite sure that Jesus is the Christ, but his death will harm no-one, at least when, as you say, his message is complete, and if he is who he says he is, then his death will certainly be beneficial. I will help you,' said Caiphas.

Caiphas rose from his chair and paced around the room, his fringed garment rippling in the breeze which came in through the slit in the wall. He paused by the slit, turned and laughed.

'Well, we have the scapegoat of Yom Kippur so your idea is not so absurd, but look, I have some thoughts about this man's death. It is no good trying to convert the scribes and Pharisees to acknowledge the Christ, they are too set in their ways, although in council they will certainly agree to his death, which is to our advantage. It is additionally to our advantage in that if they were to believe in him, they would never agree to his death. I have said that I am not sure, but I am almost won over by you. That being the case, let us consider the effect of his death on future generations. Do you remember the man who was killed by being drowned secretly in a river? Or do you remember the notorious criminal who was given a public execution and made a speech? It is the latter, is it not? Then martyrs are better remembered than others. I therefore recommend that the death of Jesus should occur as publicly and as horribly as possible...'

Judas protested.

'Remember I am doing this for future generations, and Jesus will not be too distressed if he is who he says he is – he has eternal life to look forward to. I will arrange, additionally, that a crowd of those who despise him will be present at his death to make future Christians, through their anger, unite in indignation. The method I propose is crucifixion...'

'No!' Judas shouted.

'Judas Iscariot, I admire you greatly, but you are too soft-hearted, you think too much in the short term. The matter – save one detail, your betrayal of him – is out of your hands now.'

'Alright, I won't go back on it.'

'It is important that future generations shall not know our motives; they will think more highly of Jesus. My conscience as a Jew is hurt by this action we propose; it perhaps means that Jews who, through not having met Jesus, do not convert, may not gain everlasting bliss. By killing Jesus before his time, we may effectively condemn people to hell.'

'I had not thought of that.'

'If the movement of Christianity is ever successful, Jews will be persecuted in times to come. However, Jesus preaches love, so it may not happen.'

'How can *we* crucify Christ?'

'I know a way. We ensure that he is handed over to the Romans. Pontius Pilate is a good man, but he is weak, and if he hears an angry crowd outside his window, he will sue for peace. I am sure of this. He has done it before, several times. When shall we arrange this matter?'

Judas was silent for a moment, because he was heavy-hearted. 'We, the Christ and ourselves, will undoubtedly come to Jerusalem for the Feast of the Passover. I suggest that you take the Christ then. I will lead your people to him.'

'Let it be done.'

Judas returned to the disciples, knowing that Jesus knew of his conversation with Caiphas. He was not a good dissembler but he hid his guilt as best he could. The thirteen continued their work, as before, but there was one occasion when Judas doubted his mission. They came to a fig tree, and Jesus, being hungry, put his hand up for a fig. There were no figs on the tree. Jesus then caused the tree to wither and die. The other disciples marvelled at this, but Judas thought to himself: if Jesus is Christ, how can he act so childishly? This is like a tantrum. He wondered whether, after all, he would be responsible for the death of an exceptional but not divine man, and this worried him; it would be a sin. He worried too, that the consequences would not be those he hoped for. But then he consoled himself by thinking that if the Christ were false, he deserved to die.

When they were by the sea of Galilee, Simon Peter was talking to Jesus.

'We believe, and we are sure, that you are the Christ, the son of the living God.'

'Have I not chosen you twelve, and one of you is a devil?' Jesus said, laughing. Simon Peter did not understand, but the disciples were used to Jesus saying things they didn't understand.

After Galilee, where it became unsafe for them, they went via the Mount of Olives to Bethany, where Jesus raised Lazarus from the dead. Following this event, many priests and scribes went to Caiphas to talk with him against Jesus. They said,

'What do we? For this man does many miracles. If we let him alone, all men will believe him, and the Romans will come and take away our place and our nation.'

Caiphas hid his motives and answered, without however speaking falsehood, 'Ye know nothing at all. It is expedient that one man should die for the people, and that the whole nation does not perish. And not for that nation only, but that also he should gather together in one the children of God that are scattered abroad.'

To avoid more trouble, Jesus and his party departed to Ephraim. As Judas had predicted, or possibly as Jesus, in consideration of humankind, agreed, the party set out from Ephraim to Jerusalem. They passed again through Bethany, dining with the family of Lazarus and then went on to Bethphage, from where Jesus acquired and rode a donkey. In Jerusalem Jesus celebrated the Passover with his disciples and spoke to them again of his betrayal by one of their number. They each asked, 'Is it I?' But Jesus would not tell them directly. The events of the next day are known. Judas, notwithstanding his reason, was overcome by guilt and anguish; he could not bear to have brought about the death of Jesus, however good it might be for the world. He killed himself.

If Jesus was the Christ, he was undoubtedly necessary for our wellbeing, both as regards his message and the consequences of his death. But cannot it be said that Judas, although not so great, in doing what he did, was himself worthy of our admiration?

28/05/1986

The Hunt for the Grail

THE HUNT FOR THE GRAIL

This is an extract from Mark's first novella, a picaresque account featuring thinly disguised versions of many of his York friends and acquaintances – Ed.

There was an overpowering smell of cat urine. If you were charitable you could say that it was the smell of elderflowers but the smell was too distinctive for most charity. Imbued by the smell was a room. The room thrived on the smell and it was an unusual room in this respect and many others.

Although there was bright sunshine outside, the curtains, pegged to a length of string, were pulled across the windows. Here and there a chink of light showed through them where a cat's claws had lacerated them in an upward climb. Being yellow, the curtains imparted to the room a mellow gloom such as might also occur in a store-room where there is a narrow slit for light. The walls were papered. On the paper were depicted hedgehogs and badgers in human dress, drinking tea outside a cosy-looking house. Looking carefully at the wallpaper you understood the immense effort that had gone into its positioning. The wallpaper was pasted in small strips about a foot long and otherwise irregular in shape. Where there was a picture on the wall (and there were many), the paper was carefully cut to stick around the picture. The pictures were hand-painted and were of variously, Roman centurions, beaches with palm trees on them, but mostly cats and dogs in complicated positions. The legs of most of the animals appeared to be made of rubber in that they curved this way and that without relation to joints. Nevertheless the dogs were so dog-like that you wanted to hug them and give in to the appeal of their smiling faces; likewise the cats were so cat-like that if there had been a ball of string let loose in the room the cats would have sprung from the picture purring. In a naïve way the essences of cats and dogs were captured.

There were other pictures on the walls, postcards and cuttings from magazines. Above the head of the bed a picture of an angel was next to pictures of nude women with their legs open. Pictures of Handel and Beethoven kept company with advertisements for lingerie. The books on the windowsill were in similar contrast and alongside Dante's Inferno was a book by Enid Blyton, the two presumably being equivalent in the reader's mind. A statue of Napoleon stood on the mantelpiece painted in garish colours, the plastic back melted in some accident with heat. Uppermost on the pile of records was a 78 of 'The Dance of the Sugar Plum Fairy' while, just peeping over the edge of this, the wild eyes of Beethoven stared. Beside the greying double bed which the occupant slept in there was another mattress on the floor, presumably for the cats, at least judging by its appearance, or maybe for visitors – although most visitors would no doubt be wary of this ancient sponge.

The room was cluttered with furniture, all of it covered in small piles of paper and oddments arranged in neat heaps at right angles to each other. A great deal of care had gone into this arrangement, and although the over-all effect of this was chaos, there was actually considerable order. The result of all this clutter was that there was only floor space immediately on entering the room and beside the bed, this pathway being all the move-ment desired by the occupant. Even so, part of this space was filled with torn-up newspapers where the cats defecated until they got fed up and did it somewhere else. From this room there was a passage lit by a small green light bulb and cluttered with junk, defunct electric fires, stools, piles of newspapers, a typewriter covered in something that looked like bread pud-ding, and many other things. Around the corner was the kitchen.

The kitchen was the nerve centre of the flat, the place where most liv-ing was done. Being three o'clock in the afternoon, the occupant was awake and sitting in it. If the bedroom was cluttered, the kitchen was even more so, a concentration of all that was in the other room. The wall was thick with pictures and additionally with photographs, mostly fairly dark as they were taken indoors without a flash. Out of near darkness the face of the occupant stared through a harlequin mask with a whitened face and painted lips. Other photographs had been taken from the window on one of the rare occasions when the curtains were pulled back: views of other blocks of flats through the mist. There were two work surfaces in the kitchen: one was covered with dead or decomposing plants, and the other was covered with stacks of margarine tubs, hundreds of them, each hav-ing been carefully balanced on its pile when it became empty.

On the floor and on every available shelf, poking out of the cupboards, were empty milk bottles, roughly two hundred of them, and a similar collection of evil-smelling, empty tins was squashed into the remaining spaces. On the windowsill a pile of broken crockery stood, artistically arranged, kept as a remainder of a famous rage, symbolising anger at society. There was a fridge, which didn't work, a pile of cushions, an electric fire which was switched on full despite the sunshine outside and two chairs, on one of which sat the occupant, Gerald.

Gerald was small and thin and did not dominate the cubicle-like space of the kitchen; rather he blended with its dinginess. His face had fine, almost Slavic features and was roughly clean-shaven. His hair was long and dyed black, matted with lumps which he kept pulling at. If there was any expression on the face it was one of discontentment. He kept rubbing persistently at his right hand in an effort to keep warm. In fact there were beads of sweat on his face, but how warm Gerald felt did not bear much relation to the surrounding temperature. He might have all the windows open in winter and still feel warm. As he rubbed his knee, his hitched-up trouser leg revealed the nylon tights he was wearing. On the opposite wall centrally there was a large painting of a golden chalice painted in yellow with rays of light emanating from it. Gerald sat in this way for a long time, perfectly still except for his right arm which moved almost apart from himself. He was lost in thought or the dull blackness which passes for thought.

There was a knock at the door. Gerald paused, listening…it came again. Slowly he left his seat and answered the door. The newcomer said 'Hello,' but Gerald turned without speaking and went back to his chair. Robbie came in and sat down. He stared at Gerald intently, bent forward on his chair with his coat huddled around him. The couple remained this way for several minutes. Finally Gerald spoke.

'One man on his own neither right nor wrong,' he said. He was quiet again.

Robbie's face lifted up a fraction as Gerald spoke and remained at this angle, staring even more intently at Gerald. Gerald ceased moving altogether. This continued for another half an hour. Robbie suddenly lurched to his feet and made for the front door. Robbie left and Gerald resumed rubbing his knee.

But Gerald was not left completely alone. Scuttling in the bath in a pile of hay was a hedgehog. Found wandering along the High Street at night, Gerald had rescued it from the motor cars and brought it back. The hedgehog wandered from one end of the bath to the other.

Outside, the sun had gone behind clouds from which a thin drizzle fell. Robbie waded through this drizzle in long strides, his body bent forward and his long coat flapping in the breeze. He went along the main road for some time, and then disappeared into a maze of back streets.

Back at the flat, after another hour or so Gerald moved. He fetched from the other room a colouring book, in which were the outlines of trees and birds ready to fill in. After much scuffling around on his seat Gerald began to work on the book. He used for this purpose a brush with almost no hairs on it, and despite the pictures demanding large expanses of the same colour, proceeded to fill in the pictures one tiny stroke at a time. He concentrated intensely, pausing for a while after each stroke. Not even stopping to eat, he worked at the picture through the evening and into the night.

Professor Norwald Etwas Thynne sat in his room in a comfortable and dilapidated armchair, a pile of luscious meringues beside him on a small table. As with Gerald's room the walls were covered with pictures. They were much different from Gerald's, though. The pictures were wild and turbulent. They were heavy with black, through which shone incandescent reds and blues. They were full of action, unlike the classical simplicity of Gerald's cats and gods. Each one was signed with a large black signature and some had titles scrawled in black paint across the bottom. One was 'Mother'. Another was 'The Last Supper'. One wall was lined with books – all large and black with gold lettering on their spines. There were books in Latin and French, books in ancient English and books of Hieroglyphs. Nearest to him by his chair were a set of particularly large books with 'Wagner' printed lengthways on them. There was a space in the shelf here and one of the books lay open on Professor Thynne's lap. The table and bed were covered in more books and writings, the floor too. The books on the floor practically adhered to it, glued by the residue of many fallen meringues and cream cakes.

The professor had a shock of wild white hair which sprang radially from his head. His eyes gave his face a look of constant surprise. His lips were full and moist, and grey stubble sprouted from his cheeks and chin, which was double. Underneath a black waistcoat a considerable paunch bulged out. He was not tall.

His living was confined to this one room. In the past he'd had a mansion in London decked with many original paintings and icons, sculptures by well-known sculptors, and been at the centre of literary life. But something 'had happened' and now he was bound to this room, living on a small extract from the family riches. His mind however was too active to be lonely, and recoiled under the shock of vast historic conflagrations. Empires tossed and turned in his skull as effortlessly as a shopping list does in others'. Gigantic schemes and quests juggled in his brain for attention. His brain was awash with a nightmare of knowledge, and this nightmare gave him pleasure. And so he sat, absorbing more knowledge, his face betraying only concentration and surprise, as he was always surprised at what he learnt. There came footsteps and a knock on the door.

'Enter,' he declaimed.

Robbie came in and stood looking around, giving the appearance of being lost.

'Are you a homosexual?' the professor said.

'No. I just jerk off.'

'Oh, I haven't the imagination,' the professor said sadly. He continued: 'Did you know that Stalin trained to be a priest?'

'No, I didn't. That's amazing.'

'Yes, yes it is rather. Perhaps someone will find that Mussolini trained to be a pantomime actor, or Jesus trained to be a boxer. Did you know that Gladstone chewed each mouthful of food precisely thirty-seven times?'

'No, I didn't.'

'What do you know then?'

Robbie shrugged his shoulders.

'Do you speak French?'

'Yes, I do.'

There followed a long conversation in French. Professor Thynne moved from his chair and paced up and down the room, gesturing theatrically with his left hand. 'Splendid, you're my intellectual equal,' he said, hugging Robbie. 'Tell me, do you know Gerald Hagenbach?'

'Yes, I went to see him yesterday.'

'And how did you find him?'

'Well, fine, but he didn't say much.'

'Ah, up to his old tricks I suppose.'

'He said that one man on his own is neither right nor wrong.'

'Very true – how profound. Your name, by the way? What is your name?'

'Robbie.'

'Very good. Gerald is quite quite deluded, you know. He thinks I practise influences at a distance on him.'

'Really?'

'Oh yes. He says I'm in league with the forces of darkness. How could
I be? I'm very fond of the dear boy. It's very painful to me. You couldn't
intercede with him on my behalf, could you?'

'Yes, I could try.'

'Thank you so much. You see I need the company of fellow visionar-
ies such as Gerald. Such vision I… I haven't the word for it in English.
German is so much better in such cases. Can you speak German?'

'No, 'fraid not.'

'Oh' said the professor, genuinely disappointed. 'He's a repository of
the Zeitgeist. All that is good and evil in this society filters through him
and is transformed into expression of pure spirit,' the professor continued. 'His Weltanschauung is rather gloomy at times, I fear, but that is his
prerogative. Schopenhauer…many men of genius were gloomy.'

'You compare Gerald with Schopenhauer?' said Robbie, amazed.

'Yes, of course, why not?' he demanded.

Robbie was silent.

'Of course, Gerald is rather more intuitive than logical but that's the
only difference. In this age of machines and technology we need his intu-
ition.'

'Well, all I can say is that I've never thought of Gerald in that way.'

'Well, you should. Have you examined his face? If the end of society is
the removal of contradictions, there is something primitive in his face.
The impact of good and evil has left scars on him.'

'Can't say I've noticed.'

'Poor Gerald, he takes the whole world on his shoulders. Has he told
you he comes from Holland?'

'He told me that his surname, Hagenbach, was derived from Den
Haag and that his ancestors must have been members of the Dutch par-
liament.'

'Tell me, are you middle class?'

'I guess so.'

'I thought as much. I have a tremendous sympathy for the lower middle classes. My friend Tristan comes from the lower middle classes. Of
course, I've been ostracised by all my old friends as a result but what do I
care when true friendship is on the board?'

'That's terrible.'

'Yes, I've been let down abominably. You must leave me now, I need to
be alone.'

Robbie turned abruptly to go, and as he left his feet brought the carpet
up with them at each step. 'Oh, goodbye,' he said. 'I almost forgot.'

'Very well. Goodbye,' said Professor Thynne, already looking in the opposite direction and absorbed in some new train of thought.

Back at his home, Robbie lay down on the sofa. After a while he began to repeat the name of the avatar Baba. He repeated it for many hours. This cured him of all sickness.

Meanwhile, at a flat on the outskirts of town, Alec brooded. The room he was in was fit for brooding, certainly it was not a place for scintillating thought. It was cold and damp and full of furniture. There was two of everything, two tables, two chairs, two sofas, two beds. There was very little room to move around in. The walls were painted in an old shabby green and festooned with spiders' webs.

The considerable bulk of Alec was positioned centrally in an old green armchair. He smoked. Opposite him was a television at which he appeared to stare although it was not switched on. His face was bulky also, decorated by a thin stream of beard which trickled down from each side of his mouth. A great conflict occupied his mind, whether to do something or not. Despairing of solving the problem, he turned to God for advice.

'God, should I go shopping?'

God said, 'No.'

'God, should I clean up the kitchen?'

Again God said, 'No.'

His face turned upward and the pupils of his eyes disappeared also upward. 'God, should I score some dope?'

This time God said, 'Yes.'

Shaken by this contact with the Divine, Alec remained in his chair looking down. Finally, cautiously, and with much effort, he stood up and went to the front door in a dreamlike state, moving with a kind of floating action. But he stopped still in the movement of walking and, very slowly indeed, turned around. He went back to his chair in the main room. From under a table he produced a set of bulky folders entitled 'Dreams', the record of ten years of dreaming, and sat with them on his lap. There were many fine dreams here. The collection was marred, though, by the illegibility of many dreams scribbled down in moments of half-waking. There were dreams of spiders, monsters and previous reincarnations.

Alec shuffled through them wistfully but at last came to one with the bold legend, 'Pygmies eat my right foot!' His brows furrowed with concentration. He read the dream and relived the experience. One dream led to another and so he sat engrossed.

The following day Gerald decided to go and see Professor Thynne. More precisely, he was moved to go and see the professor. The expedition had begun with an oscillating movement to the front door and back to the kitchen. The amplitude of the oscillations had increased until he found himself outside the front door.

Gerald moved towards the professor's house. He had something of the movement of a cat in a hurry. Although his legs moved swiftly in small steps, his body remained motionless without movement up and down. The collar of his long coat was pulled up and he darted glances this way and that as he walked. One arm was held to his body supporting the nest of possessions inside his coat. With him he carried a tape recorder, a bag of flour and a small peg doll, dressed in Swiss costume. From the outside it would be difficult to understand the bravery of his progress. Believing that all the people of the town were in active conspiracy against him, he had enormous bravery to even walk down the street. He was clearly ill at ease, though, and despite his small steps he moved with great swiftness.

On the stairs of the professor's house, he paused briefly. From the professor's room came the words of the fascist salute. Gerald continued and entered the room without knocking. Professor Norwald Thynne was standing in front of a mirror with one arm raised. Hearing the intrusion, he turned and without surprise said: 'Ah, Gerald, it's very good to see you.' Gerald's eyes strayed towards a plate of buns and seeing this the professor said: 'Would you like a cream cake?' But even as he said it, Gerald had darted towards the plate and stood bent over it, cramming in a bun with both hands. 'Oh,' the professor said, watching him.

'Yes please,' mumbled Gerald when he had finished.

'Have you brought me anything, a prophecy for instance?' the professor said, hands behind his back. Gerald brought out the peg doll.

'Very nice,' said the professor, embarrassed.

'Wait a minute,' said Gerald and brought out a collection of grubby papers from his pocket. With great care he handed one to the professor. Professor Thynne moved over to his chair and sat down, swinging a lamp over the chair. He read:

I saw a ghost
Eating toast
Halfway up a lamp-post
It was the ghost of EXISTENCE.

His forehead wrinkled. Holding the paper up away from his head, the professor declaimed the poem with expressive motions of his left hand. 'What did you think of that. What?' he said. 'Brings it to life, don't you think?' He paused. 'But this is wonderful, Gerald, truly wonderful. Your poem is redolent to me. It expresses the existential angst of our age. Existence is truly a ghost in these ravaged times of ours. Ah, poetry, Gerald, poetry. Give me poetry. Do you know the poetry of Ezra Pound?'

Gerald made no move to reply.

'Some people find Pound difficult to understand. Of course, if they don't know the whole of ancient Chinese literature, Greek mythology, Italian Renaissance history and modern psychology, then they would.' He paused and looked at Gerald drily. 'I don't find him at all difficult.' Gerald was busy scratching himself, though. Undeterred, the professor continued: 'Well, this is a splendid day, we must celebrate.

Would you like some coleslaw? Or perhaps sauerkraut?' he said with a German accent.

'You are evil,' Gerald said.

'I most certainly am not.'

'You are evil because you use too much black in your paintings. And you use red. You don't find red in nature. Red is the colour of blood and death. Black and red equals death. You worship death. Where I live all the windows and doors are painted red. What are they trying to do to us? It's like Auschwitz. They sit there in their cosy offices thinking, "Aha, what shall we do to make them suffer?" "Easy," says the Führer, "we'll paint the bloody houses red". It's like that song I wrote.'

'You wrote a song?' the professor asked hopefully.

Gerald brought out the tape recorder and after pressing various buttons stood back from it with a triumphant air. After something unintelligible in a Scottish accent a monotone voice came from the recorder.

Auschwitz and Belsen
Belsen and Auschwitz
The skeleton crew
What is a stripe-pyjama'd
Negro to you?

The song was sung to the accompaniment of two inversions of the same major chord repeated alternatively – 'ding dong ding dong.' This innocent background somehow served to escalate the menace of the song.

And the National Front band play
On the promenade prom prom
And how do you do?

'Oh, Gerald, turn it off, I can't stand it,' the professor said.

Gerald switched it off with a mischievous smile. The professor rubbed his forehead. 'So you see,' said Gerald energetically, 'that's what it's like where I live. They're all fascists, every man Jack of them. And you are too!'

The professor gurgled. 'Gerald, this is too much. However have you got this idea of me? You make me sad. You must have more faith in humankind.'

'Humankind is rotten. It doesn't deserve faith.'

'But you must admit there is goodness in the world. Do you remember, for instance, when Tristan gave you some sweets on that day when I held your hand when you were upset? Do you?'

'When will people be sincere?' Gerald demanded, beginning to enjoy himself. 'I have said that "when people are sincere there will be no more people left".'

'What about the Holy Grail?' asked the professor.

'The Holy Grail is filth,' Gerald said.

'But you did that marvellous picture of it,' the professor remonstrated.

'Yes, but I've changed my mind,' muttered Gerald, not convinced with himself.

'We must find the Holy Grail. That will restore the faith of humankind,' said the professor.

'Yes,' said Gerald.

'Good. We are agreed then.' The professor rose from his chair, paced once along the room, then came back and sat down. 'Please take a seat, Gerald. You can sit on the bed. You're not in a bus queue, you know.'

Gerald sat down.

'A cup of tea perhaps,' said the professor with a charming smile.

'Yes please.'

The professor hurried to the kitchen to make it. Gerald remained. He came back and handed Gerald a cup of tea. They both sat staring into the cups.

'What became of the Holy Grail?' the professor said ruminatively. 'What became of it after Parsifal found it?'

He deserved no answer but Gerald replied: 'I don't know.'

'Gerald, I am not evil. There is a similarity between greatness and evil. It's this confusion you're making. I merely have a great mind. And it would befit me to be the discoverer of the answer to my last question. One last great act before I grow too old for such accomplishment!'

Gerald looked at the floor.

'Yes, I would truly like to find the Grail. Eh, Gerald, what do you think?'

'Yes,' said Gerald. 'I want a girlfriend,' said Gerald.

'Don't talk to me about girls, talk about the Grail,' the professor said, gesturing expansively.

'I would like to find the Grail too, but I want a girlfriend.'

'All in good time, Gerald, all in good time. Gerald, you're intellectually capable of writing such a marvellous apostrophe to existence, surely you have some constructive ideas.'

'I want a girlfriend,' Gerald said stubbornly.

'Could it be in York, for instance?' the professor continued. 'York is a great centre for the church, great and ancient. Do you suppose it could be here?' He paused. 'Certainly we must search here, consult a priest or two, the Archbishop. But if it is, it must be being kept a secret. We must worm out the secrets.'

Gerald looked up. 'I could find it out,' he said.

'How?'

'By using my gun.'

'No, Gerald, violence won't do at all. It's contrary to the spirit of the search. There are precedents, I know. A hijacker once held a plane-load of passengers to ransom demanding to know the third secret of Fatima. But even so, Gerald, the search must elevate us as it elevated Parsifal.'

'It's only a plastic gun,' said Gerald.

'Oh, I see.'

'I could point it at them and say, "Tell me where the Grail is or I'll shoot you!"'

'No, Gerald, no!'

'And if they didn't say…!'

'Trick or treat, eh?'

'And if they still didn't say, I could put a curse on them.'

'You risk damnation.'

'So? I've been damned for years.'

'Even so, Gerald, we must approach the matter with more subtlety. For instance, I could tell him I was a direct descendent of Joseph of Arimathea, who brought the Grail to England.'

'I would shoot him.'

'I dare say the early knights of the Grail were ruthless. Parsifal is rumoured to have put a whole town to the sword for being pagan and that didn't preclude him qualifying to reach the Grail. However – a priest, Gerald, a priest!'

'A priest is not better than anyone else.'

'You would shoot anyone then, Gerald?'

'Yes. They've been making my life hell for years now. They deserve to die.'

'Gerald, where is your spirituality? I abhor violence. There must be another way.'

'Yes,' said Gerald. After a pause he began to speak. At first quietly, but rising to an excited crescendo in which he paced the room flailing his arms.

At the Tang Hall end of Melrosegate was a public lavatory. It was set back from the road in a paved forecourt and surrounding it were forsythia trees and other flowering shrubs, while the far side of it looked onto a park. From the rear windows the view was of weeping willows and a stream. Children and dogs cantered on this expanse. One patch of the grass had a bluish tinge, the effect of millions of speedwell flowers which poked between the grass blades. The building itself was about twenty feet by ten, not designed for mass use. Its roof was of pottery tiles, splashed with lichens except for the course of stone slabs which mounted its pitch at either end. The windows were covered with black boards. Inside this building Mark the marbler worked.

Mark stood motionless in front of a trough, a large brush in his hand. Not a muscle twitched. Suddenly his left arm was flung above his head and his right arm and body darted towards the trough, his right wrist vibrating from side to side as he did so. The movement was rather like that of a fencer making a lunge. He stood erect and motionless. Covering the surface of the trough in rounded spots, a thin film of colour had appeared, contrasting with the dirty size upon which it floated. He dipped the tip of another brush into a paint pot, shaking it to get just the right amount of colour on its bristles and, taking up an old wrench, knocked the stock of the brush against it. Hundreds of tiny spots appeared on top of the existing colour, each one shaded, more dense towards its centre. He knocked the brush on the wrench until almost all the surface appeared to be covered. The wall beyond the trough was covered in a layer of paint as a result of this exercise, even as high as the ceiling. He relaxed and stood back, looking at the surface of the size intently. His motion suddenly becoming more fluid, he went to a pile of large white papers and carried one by opposite corners to the trough. He let this down onto the size from the far corner, very gently. Almost as soon as it was down he lifted it up, again starting from the far corner. There was a paper-shaped hole in the surface of the size. All the paint from this hole adhered to the underside of the paper. He flipped the paper over, face upwards, onto a board which stood in a large sink next to the trough. Turning on the tap, he cleaned the paper of size with a jet of fine spray. Finally he took the paper carefully with both hands and carried it across the workshop to a rack of dowel rods, over one of which he hung it. He bent down and looked at the paper closely. His breath now came more freely. Standing back he clapped his hands, danced a few steps and started singing what sounded like a Russian folk tune.

The man, Mark, was in his late twenties. He wore an artist's smock and paint spattered blue jeans. His hair was wild and wavy, although not long, and a crescent-shape curl hung over his forehead. His eyes were deep and overhung with large black eyebrows. His mouth was slightly lopsided, a permanent trace of mockery about it. He had a large chin which was clean-shaven.

Although it was light outside, the workshop was lit by electric light and all the windows, except two at the rear, blocked with boards. This enabled him to concentrate better, and put off curious passers-by from looking in and interrupting.

Inside the building there were still traces of its original function. The walls were covered to head height with yellow tiles. The original cubicles were hidden, reduced to thigh height and supporting work surfaces. One cubicle, however, had been retained 'for old times' sake'. There were shelves with paints and oils on, chemicals and the big bag of carragheen moss seaweed with which the size was made. The workshop was painted white, except for the woodwork which was painted a warm rusty red. Racks of papers completed and coated with glue size stood ready to make up orders, and more papers, yet to be completed, hung from the ceiling where they had been hoisted by a pulley.

This workshop was a secret place. Derelict so far as outsiders were concerned, it yielded activity and beauty to those who knew it. It was a haven to Mark. In this place he knew both great excitement and great calm, great discovery, amazement, and many original thoughts. Few people came to disturb him here; an occasional child more curious or brave than the rest would knock at the door and ask what went on there, perhaps try to steal his cigarettes. One child had come saying, 'Is this a sex shop, mister?' Other adults came from time to time, demanding to use the lavatory and refusing to believe that it was a workshop.

Mark went into action again. After six sheets, which took him almost an hour, he sat down and rolled a cigarette. The day was divided up in this way, with the occasional cup of coffee to accompany the cigarette.

After six hours of marbling the size was too depleted and muddy for further use, and so Mark emptied the remainder and scrubbed the trough, mopped the floor and packed up. Before leaving he gave the marbled papers one last look, and then turned. He slammed the door and set off to walk home.

Gerald had found a new word. He had found it in a Victorian book he'd bought in a junk shop. The word fascinated him. It was written out on a slip of paper which he fidgeted with. He turned the word this way and that, upside down and face down. He wondered what it could mean. The word was 'effulgent'. It was an impressive word, bound to mean something important, and Gerald resolved to use it in his next piece of writing.

The telephone rang. Mark answered it.

'Hello, this is Andrew. I'm quite close to you now. I thought I'd just ring you and warn you that I'm on my way to your place.'

'Oh no,' Mark said.

'I'm sorry but I can't help it. I only come to you out of desperation.'

'OK,' said Mark, sighing.

'Well, I'll see you soon. Goodbye and God bless you.'

Mark put the phone down heavily and wandered about the room sullenly with his hands in his pockets. By contrast with the other places we've been in, Mark's house was quite ordinary. It was light and dry. A piano stood against one wall and a bicycle near the door. There was a richly coloured if threadbare carpet on the floor and a clean welcoming-looking sofa. About this room there was more evidence of the twentieth century: a telephone, a record player, and general cleanliness and lack of clutter.

Mark had been interrupted in one of his usual pastimes outside the workshop, telepathising. He was in constant contact with a man who had so far not revealed himself, a man who had put Mark into this state of being telepathic. Mark's messages were generally pleas to be freed from this state, either to God or to this man. Mark was jealous of the time spent in this way and resented intrusions. Electronic noises played in his left ear, making sleep difficult, and constantly reminding him that he was not free. Mark also suspected that this 'man' could see through his eyes and followed Mark's living in the manner of watching a television or a puppet show.

Twenty minutes later there was a knock at the rear door. Mark answered it.

'Hello, hello,' said Andrew breathlessly.

'Hello,' said Mark sourly. 'Why do you always come in at the back door?' he asked.

'So as not to be seen. No, it's an old country custom,' Andrew said, removing one of his several layers of clothing. 'Oh sweet angels,' he said, 'I've had such a time hitching. I waited two and a half hours at a motorway café. But do you know, the man that actually stopped, I heard a voice calling out "Come on Andrew" and it was a man who'd given me a lift a previous time I was hitching. He said, "Any time, Andrew. Any time". Thank heaven's there's still some goodness left in humanity.'

Meanwhile, Andrew's dog, Jock, had extracted a slipper from Andrew's open case and was rushing up and down the room growling and shaking it to and fro. 'Oh, come on, Jock. I want to wear that,' Andrew said, looking good-humouredly at Jock. 'Anyway, he took me to the York turn off, and almost immediately an army man stopped and picked me up. He was going to Acomb but he took me all the way to Melrosegate. Wasn't that good of him? Now wait a moment, I'll just sort myself out a bit and feed Jock.' He rummaged through the suitcase. 'Do you know,' he said, 'I've got three pairs of trousers on including these nylon over-trousers, and two pullovers. I had a desperately difficult time trying to have a pee at the York turn-off, and it was bitterly cold on the road. Jock, though, he was as good as gold. He sat there patiently without a murmur. Or course, I have to keep him on a lead otherwise he'll chase the motor cars. You know, Mark, I think of you a lot. I pray for you every day!'

'I wondered what had been going wrong,' Mark said.

Andrew chortled. 'Now, now, Mark. Mind you, I have another friend who says "Stop interfering in my life" when I tell him I've been praying for him.'

'Well, thank you, I suppose,' said Mark.

'Did you read those books I left here last time?' Andrew asked.

'No, they were children's books,'

'Yes, I know, but I do love reading children's books; it's a more inno-cent and better world that's portrayed.'

'I gave them to the Oxfam shop.'

Andrew removed some of the extra layers of garments he was wear-ing, then stood up. He was slightly built, but rounded and rather jolly-looking. His face was round and there was a tuft of hair on top which had earned him the nickname of Tintin at the school where he had once taught. He was middle-aged. 'How have you been, then, Mark?' he said.

'Oh, alright, the usual.'

'You should try praying, you know. Prayer works. It's been proven many times.'

'I have tried praying, for almost a year now.'

'You've kept very quiet about it. Any answer?'

'No, and sometimes I've prayed all day even. If there was a doctor on earth who refused to give a cure he could easily give, he would be struck off the list and called criminally negligent. I'm coming to the conclusion that God, if God exists, is a criminal. God either doesn't exist or doesn't care. I think God doesn't exist.'

'The fool has said in his heart "There is no God,"' Andrew quoted.

'You find Biblical justification to call me a fool. I don't call you a fool.'

'If God hasn't helped you there's probably a good reason for it.'

'Don't make excuses for God.'

'How have you prayed?'

'Adequately.'

'Well, don't give up. Help will come.'

Mark snorted. He said: 'I can understand, with your homelessness and pennilessness, that "God" helps you to keep going when many others would have given up, so I don't begrudge your faith, but all the same I must think you're deluded.'

'I most certainly am not.'

'If God exists, God gave us reason and that reason teaches us to want evidence before we believe in something. Give me one shred of evidence, then I'll believe.'

'You'll learn, boy. You'll learn.'

Andrew took from his case a bottle of holy water, a crucifix and a fluo-rescent plastic statue of the Madonna. He took these upstairs to the room where he would sleep. The crucifix he stuck to the wall above the bed, the Madonna stood on a table next to it, and he sprinkled drops of holy water in a circle around the bed. He came downstairs again.

'Holy water.' said Mark 'Go on, tell me you use it for shaving each morning.'

Andrew grinned. 'I use it to protect the place from the Devil.'

'If you had your way, they'd be selling holy waters in the supermarkets and broadcasting hymn tunes for muzak.'

'Blasphemy!' Andrew said.

Mark laughed.

'Look here, can I use some of your vegetables, Mark, I haven't a penny on me.'

'OK then.'

'I'll feed the dog first. Jock! Come here, Jock, there's a good dog.'

Jock was a black and extremely hairy dog of somewhat unusual appearance. His legs were short and stout and his body, in contrast, was very long, and, to compensate for the length, arched in the middle. Jock stood growling, looking into the empty food pot. He was fed. Andrew then moved to peel some potatoes. As he peeled them under the tap he whistled tunelessly to himself and muttered. 'Sweet angels and saints, shit!' he said. 'I've cut my thumb. Have you a bandage?'

The meal was eaten quickly. Andrew turned on the radio and listened to some music but turned it off quickly. 'Ugh, modern music,' he said. 'Have you any news, Mark? How's Alec?'

'Alec's alright, except he's having difficulty with Tina, who's moved in there for a spell.'

'Yes, Tina is much too much of a handful for Alex. How about Gerald?'

'Well, Gerald and Etwas Thynne have cooked up some scheme to find the Holy Grail.'

'Have they now, the little blighters? But what fun!'

'They're looking for it in York.'

Andrew laughed. 'Oh, Gerald, whatever will he think of next. The Grail is only in legend, it never existed. Joseph of Arimathea never came to England.'

'I don't know, but if Professor Thynne believes it I'm tempted to go along with it. I respect his erudition.'

'Rubbish! The scheme is crazy. I tell you what, though,' he said after a pause. 'If you did find the Grail, *you* find the Grail, wouldn't it give you the evidence you need to believe in God?'

'Maybe, but the existence of the Grail doesn't prove the existence of God.'

'I think if you were to behold it, as it's reputed to have been, radiant with light, you would believe in God.'

'What is the Grail anyway?'

'It is the chalice from which Christ drank at the Last Supper. Supposedly it contains Christ's blood.'

'Oh, I thought it was more mystical than that.'

'It's mystical enough, but go on Mark, why not have a go? You look for it as well.'

'I thought you didn't believe in it.'

'Well, not really, but there's often substance to these old legends. It's worth looking into. I might consider it myself. It would give life some purpose!'

'Well, if it would provide evidence of God's existence, I would like to see it. I would like to believe in God but it's so absurd.'

'What's absurd about God?'

'A being who can simultaneously know the contents intimately of the minds of millions of people. Of course it's absurd, or incredible.'

'But what if it were true?'

'If it were true it would be wonderful. It would change my life.'

'Well then.'

'Well then, I suppose if God's existence would mean so much to me it's worth following – even a tiny clue which would betray it.'

'Exactly.'

'But to spend a great deal of time on what might turn out to be a wild goose chase?'

'Why not? You can spare the time.'

'I'm not so sure.'

'Custodian of the Holy Grail. Think what that would do to your life. Or mine for that matter.'

'There'd be thousands of pilgrims queuing at my front door for a sight of it. I'd have to make the place into a fortress to protect it.'

'There is that, of course.' Andrew paused. 'It might change the world. Think what impact of seeing it would be on the members of the Soviet Politburo.'

'Yes, it could change society. At the moment pilgrims worship some piece of rubbish which is supposed to be Christ's foreskin. If there was some true relic, undoubtedly true…'

'It's a thought, isn't it? We must have a word with Gerald and Professor Thynne.'

Dianna lay on her bed making love to an invisible God. We will grant her privacy in this. The God visited her only occasionally, sometimes to impart advice but otherwise for more intimate communion. The God responded to the name of Ravtasher and was one of Dianna's closest companions. He guided her through daytime and caressed her at night, sometimes getting in the way of other union. There was another God called Dok who sometimes came to her but he was evil, and she fought his presence with spells and grains of rice. Dianna got out of bed and walked naked into the other room. She pulled the curtains, and sat in front of the fire. She took up a book called 'The Lotus in the Garden' and began to read.

The room was sparsely furnished but somehow cluttered. It had never been moved into properly. The floor of lino was still uncovered except for some scraps of carpet, on one of which Dianna sat. There were piles of magazines and papers, library books long since overdue and collections of dried flowers that sprouted from many jam-jars positioned around the room. There was a heavy smell of incense.

There was a knock on the door. Dianna put down the book with a sigh and answered it. She was just about to open the door when she realised she had nothing on.

'Just a moment, I've got no clothes on,' she shouted.

'OK,' said a voice.

She came back with a blanket around her and opened the door. It was Robbie.

'Hello Robbie.'

'Watcha Dianna. How are you?'

'Oh, you know,' said Dianna.

They went back into the other room and Diana turned the fire up, as if two people needed twice as much heat.

'How about a cup of coffee?' Robbie said.

'Oh, alright.'

'Thanks. Ta.'

Dianna came back with two expensive-looking porcelain cups and sat cross-legged in front of the fire.

'I've just been to see Gerald,' Robbie said.

'Uh huh.'

'He's got some scheme to find the Holy Grail.'

Andrew went to see Gerald. Jock took him there. Seeming to know the way, Jock strained at the leash, forcing Andrew to lean backwards. It was a short distance but on the way they had a minor mishap, as Jock mistook a man's leg for a lamppost. On the stairs to Gerald's flat Andrew paused. The smell of cats penetrated, even through the narrow crack of the door, outside and down the stairs. Andrew grimaced. He knocked at the door and shouted through the letterbox for a long time, having to rouse Gerald from bed. As the door finally opened two cats attempted to rush out but were captured by Gerald and brought back in. Inside, Jock stood in front of the cats and wagged his tail. The cats responded by touching noses with him. In the cramped space of the kitchen, Andrew sat down slightly unhappily, fearing infection. Gerald prepared a cup of coffee, wiping the mugs on a dirty towel he'd just blown his nose on. Andrew tried to prevent this but was too late. Gerald sat down and produced a jar full of cigarette ends. He pulled the cigarettes apart to get the remaining tobacco out and slowly rolled a cigarette from these oddments. As he did so, a cat defecated noisily at his feet. Gerald looked on dispassionately.

'Gerald!' expostulated Andrew.

'What's the matter, it's only cat crap,' said Gerald.

'I'm not crazy about hygiene but really this is too much!'

'It's my flat.'

'Aye, lad, it is. Mind you, when you came to stay with me in Perth you were happy enough to have a clean room and clean clothes, as long as someone else does it, eh?'

'It's hard for a person on their own to keep a place tidy,' said Gerald awkwardly. 'Anyway, what are you doing here?' he continued.

'That's a nice way to greet someone.'

'You keep taking off around the country. You'll never find anywhere unless you stand still. You complain all the time about being homeless but it's your own damned fault. Don't come to me expecting sympathy.'

'I've come to you because I wanted to see you and I thought you might like to see me.' Gerald remained silent.

'Give us a smile, Gerald, eh?'

'Find me a girlfriend,' Gerald said, thumping the work surface violently with his fist.

'Gerald, I am neither a marriage bureau nor a pimp.'

Gerald grinned.

'If only you would tidy yourself up a bit and get rid of the smell I'm sure hundreds of girls would fall for you,' he continued.

Gerald smiled coyly.

'And look, you do as well as most people. You had a relationship with Dianna for a while, didn't you?'

'She wasn't sincere,' said Gerald, his face suddenly rigid.

'Dianna's got her own problems and she found you a bit heavy, shouting at her about the forces of darkness and light all the time.'

'It's not good having a relationship without sincerity,' said Gerald.

'No, lad. I agree but you must admit…'

'I admit nothing.'

'You never have.'

The conversation came to a halt and they both looked blankly at each other.

'How's Mark?' said Gerald, pulling at a lump of hair.

'Oh, he's fine, a bit grumpy but otherwise OK.'

Gerald nodded and started tapping his foot.

'He says you've got some idea of finding the Holy Grail,' Andrew continued.

'Mind your own business,' said Gerald. 'I've written something. Look.'

He pulled out a piece of paper from his pocket and handed it to Andrew. He read:

So hers, was that, feeling wrought, for she captured. Yes the dew, of ages. And went melting like, the freshly covered mist, and dew upon the early grass. For the Nighting-gale when with wings out-stretched. Fluttered for a considerable time. Out-stretched her wings, and took to the sky. Billowing clouds, of ancient worth. Nurtured suckling to this birth. Nurtured suckling to this violet-scented, amethyst-cool breath, upon the neck, and in the swirling flowers of worth. Whence a consecrated love, with light feathers, swirling burning, love is turning seen there in the limelight, attributes to that beauty.

'But Gerald, this is marvellous,' said Andrew, genuinely moved. 'I think this is your best writing yet. It's beautiful. What a character you are. You live in filth and stench and out comes all this beauty. You must keep writing, Gerald. Thank you. Thank you for showing it to me.'

Gerald looked pleased.

'You know, you really should try to get published.'

'How?'

'Well, send your writing to the radio or a publisher.'

'I don't want my name to be known, it's bad enough as it is. Too many people know my name. When that happens you can be sure there'll be trouble. How would you like to have your name splashed all over the cover of books?'

'I should be so lucky!'

'Luck. You have all the luck. You get people to let you stay at their places all the time, while I'm stuck here in Auschwitz.'

'I've tried, Gerald. I've tried for five years now to find a place where you can come to live with your cats and be free.'

'You don't know how to set about it. When people ask you to go, you just go. You should keep your foot in the door.'

'It's not that easy.'

'Of course it's easy. If I didn't have you dogging my footsteps all the time, I'd have found a place years ago.'

'Now, Gerald, that's not fair. I really do my best, you know.'

'Well, it's not enough. You're like someone in the British Raj. You come here with your white suit and cane, saying "Aha, what have we got here? Let's see what we can do to impose imperial order. Let the big white man rule".'

'It's not like that, Gerald, truly it isn't.'

'You're like a bloody jailer saying "Get your hair cut or we'll put you on the torture rack". You're the big fascist dictator, Andrew. That's you!'

'Give us a break, Gerald.'

'You come here saying "Let's clean him up and make him look dandy", like producing a puppet on a string. I am not a puppet on a string, I am a human being. And I have said "You should treat a human being like a human being and not like a dog".'

'I treat my dog very well, thank you.'

'You know what I mean. You try to help other people but you can't help other people until you have a place to live and something to give. You take out your own troubles on other people. You go round getting on everybody's back and making life miserable for them.' Andrew sighed. 'You're a public school snob. You go around with your God-damned British Raj accent thinking you're so much better than everybody else. But you're not better than anyone else. I'm better than you. I'm a ratepayer and a rent payer. You've got nowhere to live and you go round sponging off other people.'

'Gerald,' Andrew said gently, 'I've given you money. Yes? I've given you things when I had almost nothing at all. Yes? I've helped you out of half a dozen scrapes with the law, the authorities. If you're lonely and you ring me up, I hitchhike the length of the country to see you. And what do I get for it? A broken rib, stitches in the face.'

'It was an accident,' Gerald said.

'I can but try,' said Andrew.

'You can stick your help behind a hedge! I was doing very well until you came on the scene.'

'Oh, I give up,' said Andrew. 'For goodness sake think of something jolly and stop making life such heavy weather.'

'Would you like to hear my tapes?' Gerald said.

'No thank you,' Andrew groaned.

'Would you like some chips?' Gerald asked.

'Yes, that would be nice. I haven't eaten all day.'

Gerald washed some potatoes and sliced them over the chip pan where they squelched into the cold and fragment-filled fat. He cleaned two plates, drying them with the same unhygienic towel, while Andrew looked on forbearingly.

'You know, Gerald, I am interested in this idea of yours about the Holy Grail. If you set out to find it, can I come too?'

'You can come as well if you want. Only you've got to keep your mouth shut.'

'Alright,' Andrew laughed.

'We're going to look in York to start with and then we might try other places.'

'Have you got any other places in mind?'

'No.'

'How on earth are you going to start looking?'

'I don't know,' Gerald said.

'It's a crazy idea,' said Andrew.

'Yes,' said Gerald.

'Has Madeleine been to see you?'

'Yes.'

'Was she drunk again?'

'Yes. She took some money off me.'

'And you haven't got it back?'

'No. I had to call the police to get her out. She was being abusive to me.'

'Oh, not again.'

'Yes.'

'She must be well known around these flats.'

'She is.'

'Ah well, she's company I suppose.'

'Yes.'

The chips were ready and Gerald fished them out and put them on the plate. Then he broke two eggs into the fat. Shortly after he extracted their soggy masses and put them one on each plate.

'Would you like some tomato sauce?' Gerald asked.

'No, thank you. I'm fine as I am.'

Halfway through his plateful Gerald put it down and said: 'I've got to go into town.'

'Just a moment, I'll come with you.' Andrew gulped down his food. Minutes later they left with the dog, walked down the hill and along the main street. Gerald was silent, while Andrew talked breezily about his travels. Suddenly Gerald threw all his weight against Andrew and Andrew nearly fell in the path of a passing car.

'Sweet Lord! What are you trying to do?' he said, when he'd recovered his balance.

'It was an accident. But you mustn't steal my ideas.'

'The Grail, you mean?'

'Yes.'

'You could have killed me, Gerald.'

'Yes, I'm sorry.'

The two walked on into town.

Professor Thynne and Tristan were playing with glove puppets. They sat on the bed with a pile of books for a stage. Professor Thynne wielded a puppet with the head of a duck called Mimi and Tristan wore a puppet with the head of a rat called Riri.

'Now Mimi,' the professor said. 'Hit Riri with the spoon.'

Mimi picked up the spoon and belaboured Riri with it, while Riri put his hands over his head.

'You're upset, are you, Riri? Never mind, Mimi will kiss it better.'

Mimi touched his beak to Riri's nose. Riri wrested the spoon from Mimi and began hitting him back.

'Oh, Tristan!' the professor said.

'Fair's fair,' said Tristan.

'Oh, I see. We're quits then. Shake hands, Riri. Shake hands, Mimi.' Riri and Mimi shook hands. 'Now, Riri. Do you know the dialectic?' Riri covered his eyes with his hands. 'You don't eh? How can you hope to be a historian?'

'I am an artist,' said Riri.

'Whoever heard of a rat being an artist,' Mimi said. Again Riri covered his eyes. 'Now, don't be sad. Come, I'll wipe away your tears.'

'Whoever heard of a duck knowing the dialectic?' Riri said.

'Well, I do, of course,' said Mimi.

'You must be a very clever duck,' said Riri.

'I am. I'm immensely clever.'

'Will you teach me, Mister duck?'

'Yes, but first you must kiss my feet.' Riri bent down to the head of Mimi. Mimi kissed him. 'Ha ha, that will teach you to presume to education.'

Again Riri put his hands over his face.

'Ah, is Riri sad? Never mind. Diddums. There there.'

'You're bad,' said Riri.

'I'm terribly bad,' said Mimi.

'But I love you all the same,' said Riri.

'And I love you too, you little fool,' said Mimi.

'Well then,' said Riri.

'Well what?' said Mimi. Riri jumped on the back of Mimi and jerked back and forth. 'Oh my goodness, stop. Oh! No don't stop. Riri Riri.'

'Was that nice?' said Riri.

'Goodness gracious it was fun. Can I do it to you?'

'Yes, certainly.'

Mimi jumped on Riri's back and repeated the motion. 'Oh, Riri. I'm exhausted.'

'Is that better, Mimi?'

'Yes, it's very much better.'

There was a knock on the door.

'Damn,' said the professor.

He went to the door and answered it. Mark stood there.

'What do you want, we're busy? No, on second thoughts, come in.'

Mark stepped into the room and glanced toward the bed.

'Riri has just sodomised Mimi, and Mimi has sodomised Riri,' the professor said, beaming cherubically.

Mark laughed. 'Your puppets?' he asked.

'Yes, of course,' said the professor.

'They don't make puppets with phalluses,' said Mark.

'No, unfortunately not,' said the professor.

'Still, we have our imagination, haven't we Tristan?'

'Yes Norwald,' said Tristan.

'This room is a paean to imagination. Have we met before?'

'Yes, we have, several times,' said Mark. 'My name is Mark.'

'Oh dear, I hadn't the foggiest idea who you were. A great mind deteriorated. Mark eh? Mark of the planet Mars, the god of war. Are you a god of war come to visit us?'

'Only occasionally,' said Mark.

'Occasionally eh? Very good. And what do you do, Mark?' the professor asked. There was a long pause.

'I play the piano.'

'Ah, the piano. Schnoedel, Ivkatsky, Morris-Node. Alman Pintan, Kwang Sang Gan, Severitas. Aha?' Mark, who hadn't heard of any of these names, stood looking blankly.

'Norwald is a very clever man,' said Tristan.

'Of course, the piano is terribly outmoded today. Since Wagner invented the music drama, all other music is rather put in the shade. Ah, Wagner, Wagner!' the professor said with a heavy German accent. 'My best friend is Winifred Wagner. I go to Bayreuth every year. What do you think of that?'

'I'm not very fond of Wagner's music,' said Mark.

'Have you ever heard of Arnold Blackman? He says I have the greatest understanding of Wagner that one can have. I'm writing a great book about Wagner. It's in its third volume so far. You're not fond of Wagner? Never mind, it takes a heroic mentality to appreciate Wagner and you're obviously not a hero. What kind of music do you like?'

'Well, I quite like Schubert.'

'Ah, Schubert Lieder.'

'No, his piano music.'

'He copied Beethoven, you know.'

'I still like Schubert.'

'Have it your own way then.'

Meanwhile Tristan had put on both puppets and Mimi and Riri cuddled each other blissfully.

'You see what they're up to now? They're inseparable, those two. Do you want to join in? We've got Roro, a bear, who you might like.'

'Well, not really.'

'Oh,' said the professor disappointed.

'Tristan, make some tea for this boy,' the professor ordered.

'Yes, professor,' Tristan said meekly and went off to do so.

'What brings you to my abode?' the professor asked.

'Well, I heard that you and Gerald were thinking of looking for the Holy Grail and I'm interested too.'

'Grail…' said the professor. 'Chretien de Troyes. The first continuation. Robert de Boron. The Didot Percival. Parsifal. The Corpus Lancelot of Grail. Perlesvaux etcetera.' He looked at Mark proudly.

'I don't know much about it except that it is supposed to contain Christ's blood.'

'Rubbish. Wolfram Von Eschenbach says the Grail is a stone.'

'Well, I don't know.'

'Of course there are many accounts. Some say it was a chalice used in the Last Supper. Some say it was the bowl used in the Last Supper. Some say it contains Christ's blood, others not.'

'So it's not certain. It may contain Christ's blood.'

'Maybe,' said the professor.

'It would be easier to recognise if it was a chalice.'

'Not necessarily. The Grail is so radiant and holy that you would recognise it instantly. You would feel that you were in the presence of holiness.'

'Andrew said something like that.'

'Did he?' said the professor.

'Andrew, yes. He said I was crazy,' Mark continued. 'Do you think I'm crazy?'

'No, just a little eccentric.'

'Thank you.'

'What do you think of my pictures? They're very good, aren't they?' said the professor, gesturing around the room.

'Well, I like them but I find them rather hectic.'

'Hectic? Not at all, they're full of calm. Well, possibly they're hectic. Tristan, Mark says my paintings are hectic.' Tristan had just re-entered the room, carrying the tea.

'Yes, Norwald,' said Tristan, flinging back his long grey hair.

'Oh, I do like if when you do that,' said the professor to Tristan. 'You see that picture there? Yes, that one in the middle. That took me three days and nights to paint. I stayed awake all that time without eating. How do I do it, you may ask? I felt no fatigue. No fatigue whatsoever. The secret is this: perfect concentration is pure repose. Perfect concentration is pure repose,' he repeated.

'I'm impressed,' said Mark.

'Yes. I can keep it up for weeks if need be. You're interested in the Grail then, or Graal as it is more properly known. Funny, I once knew a truck driver called Graal. Well, if you're really interested we must join forces. Have you any ideas about it?'

'None at all,' said Mark.

'Oh, how disappointing.'

'Just a minute, I've just had one. I could ring up all the people called

Graal and ask them if they had any history of the Grail in their family.'

'Splendid idea. Splendid!'

'Or I could even ask them if they knew of its whereabouts. Someone with a name like Graal is bound to have been curious about it and tried to trace it back.'

'That's a very good idea.'

'Yes, I like it, and there can't be too many people with the name Graal.'

'But you'd have to phone all the hundreds of Graals who live in the rest of England.'

'I could do it on the cheap rate.'

'I suppose so.'

'And then we could hunt for old documents which might give us a clue. We could go to the British Museum and ask there. They're bound to have some material that we don't know about.'

'The trouble with that is that you have to have your reference available in advance, and you need to have a letter of introduction before they'll let you in,' said the professor.

'You could write me one, or you could go yourself.'

'I go? Yes, I suppose I could.'

'Or if we really get stuck, I know a cleaner who works dusting the books there. He's called Manfred. I could get Manfred to find the reference.'

'We're making progress,' said the professor. 'I could consult some of my old colleagues.'

'And we could consult the church,' said Mark.

'Gerald's already thought of that. He plans to extract the secret with a toy gun.'

'Trust Gerald.'

'And there's no way I'll stop him making a fool of himself,' the professor continued.

Mark laughed. 'I'd like to see it,' he said.

'Yes,' said the professor. He continued. 'My only idea so far is that we could search in York for it. The Grail may be connected with some ancient place of worship. We might try Glastonbury also.'

'We could try Lindisfarne and Iona, Walsingham. Andrew sometimes goes there to the religious communities.'

'Norwald, your tea's getting cold,' said Tristan.

'What do you think of all this, Tristan?' said the professor, reaching for this tea.

'It's a good idea, Norwald. I could look in Bradford.'

'Well, Tristan, I don't think Bradford's the right place to look, somehow. It's too recently established,' said the professor.

'I could look in the junk shops.'

'Well, that's something.'

'And I could do a beautiful painting of it.'

'Yes, that would help. Do so.'

'I could paint it with gold paint on the mantelpiece of a tea room.'

'Very good. Very good.'

'With my mother standing beside me.'

'Why your mother?'

'She always did like gold and silver.'

'Yes, that's one thing I've never been able to understand. It's supposed to be made of gold. Wherever would Christ get the money to buy gold? It's far more likely to have been iron or pottery, but all the legends are consistent on this point.'

Tristan rose and crossed the room to the professor. He unobtrusively tucked the professor's shirt in while the professor continued talking.

'Think of it, a pottery Grail. It wouldn't have quite the same prestige, would it? And if it were pottery, the likelihood is that it would be broken in little pieces by now. Mind you, we face a problem if the Grail is indeed gold. It could have been melted down for the metal. But no, who would do that? Only a complete ignoramus. Besides, if it radiated light and cured illness, even the simplest of fools would realise they were onto something special.'

'It cures sickness then?' said Mark.

'Certainly. But it can also destroy. Galahad died from seeing the inside of the vessel.'

'Well, if it cures sickness I've got another reason for finding it.'

'Why, are you sick? What's wrong with you?'

'I telepathise and I take on the astral bodies of other people.'

'Oh, I see. Possession, is it? Very unpleasant.'

'It's bearable, but I wish I could get rid of this state.'

'Quite so.'

'All the people I know are in need of some kind of boost. It would help us all.'

'You say Andrew's interested in this venture?'

'No, I didn't, but he is. I think he missed out on having adventures when he was young.'

'You know, the Grail could be outside this country. According to one version of the story, Parsifal left England following a boat which contained the body of the Fisher King and the Grail. If my memory is correct, this is one of the earliest stories.'

'It makes it more difficult to find.'

'Yes, but there are many versions of this story in Germany. Perhaps it went there. I could write to some of my German contacts.'

'But we must still look in England.'

'Yes, first things first, of course. Well, you follow up your ideas and I will do something as well. Andrew, Gerald, Chris – we've got a good chance between us. My word, how I'd like to find it. Wagner would have been thrilled at what we're doing.'

'All I did was ask her if she wanted to come and see my pictures. It's not as if I asked her to pull her knickers down. Anyway, I've probably got better knickers than her,' said Gerald. Dianna and Robbie laughed.

'Well, Gerald, when you ask someone to come and see your pictures, it usually has a double meaning, you know,' said Dianna.

'There's no such thing as a double meaning. I asked her an ordinary question and I wanted an ordinary reply,' said Gerald.

'Yes,' said Dianna sarcastically.

'I mean, if I asked you to come and see my pictures, you'd come, wouldn't you?'

'It's different with me.'

'Why is it different?'

'I know you.'

'It doesn't make any difference.'

'Besides, you probably would try to get to bed with me.'

'Not always.'

'Remember the last time I came. You were trying to entice me into your bedroom to have a look at your porn pictures or something?'

Gerald grinned sheepishly.

'Anyway, you probably didn't approach her in the right way,' said Dianna.

'All I said was "I like your pink dress".'

'Whose party was it, anyway?' asked Dianna.

'It was someone called Nigel I used to know a long time ago. They were all talking about religion.

'The Christian Union brigade.'

'They were all so starched and stuck up. I mean, if someone said to me "I like your frilly blouse", I'd be very pleased.'

Gerald was indeed wearing a frilly blouse. Dianna laughed.

'I like your frilly blouse, Gerald,' she said.

'But you wouldn't go to bed with me, would you?' said Gerald.

'No, Gerald.'

'Dianna, shift a bit, can you? Your hipbone is digging into me,' said Robbie, who Dianna was sitting on top of.

'Listen to this,' said Gerald, pulling down a paper from a shelf. *There were some people who could not hear the birds singing. People who were still wearing yellow stars. People who tried to discard those yellow stars. Saying we are human beings with thoughts and feelings. That all romance is not dead. When you come into the world naked and blind. When you went out of the world, naked and messed up, and despised and persecuted. How many joys were there left still?* 'What do you think?'

'Well, it's a bit gloomy' said Dianna.

'I like it Gerald – I really like it,' said Robbie.

'It's just like me,' said Gerald. 'I'm despised and persecuted. They don't like me because I'm Dutch and an artist. They say, "You little bastard, you're different from us. We're going to send you to Coventry".' He took up the paper again. '"…Trying to see through all the wrong all the falseness. To see through all the racial hatred. Who were sent to Coventry by everybody else? Who stayed in Coventry? The mass capitalistic machine of society, throwing abuse because they were ignorant of the workings of the mind of innocent people." You see, it's just like that,' he said.

'Yes Gerald,' said Dianna, sighing.

'I've been sitting here for three years and not one of them comes to see me,' said Gerald.

'Well, we've come to see you and there's Mark, Andrew, Alec, Chris, Madeline. You get as many visitors as most people,' said Dianna.

'I mean the people round about me,' said Gerald.

'Well, I'm in my flat in Acomb and no-one whatsoever comes to see me. I'm far worse off than you, Gerald.'

'Yes, but with you it's your own fault. You won't be sincere. How can you expect people to come and see you when you aren't sincere? I mean you used to be my girlfriend but you're with Robbie now. That proves you're not sincere.'

'Sincerity's different from that, Gerald.'

'No it isn't.'

'Anyway, let's talk about something else, Gerald, this is getting a bit heavy,' said Dianna.

'I saw dinosaurs down Acomb High Street,' said Dianna.

There was no answer.

'I was frightened so I went back home,' she added.

'Oh really,' said Robbie. 'That's a heavy trip.'

'Yes, it was a bit. It was all so natural, though. There they were feeding off the grass verges.'

'You should have gone and stroked them,' said Robbie.

'You've got to be joking!' said Dianna.

'I would have phoned the police,' said Robbie.

'The police wouldn't do anything about it. A dinosaur's got a perfect right to be in Acomb High Street, after all,' Dianna said.

'I s'pose you're right,' said Robbie.

Gerald switched his tape recorder on. Very loudly a plaintive voice sang out:

If I were a pirate on the ocean blue
I'd sail for a million miles
I'd sail for a million miles…

'Oh turn it down, Gerald, we're trying to talk,' said Robbie.

Gerald turned it down slightly.

'Gerald, what's this about the Holy Grail?' Dianna said.

'I'm going to find it,' said Gerald.

Dianna laughed. 'Where are you going to look? Sorting through the rubbish on the rubbish tip, I suppose?'

'No.'

'Go and ask a policeman?'

'The police are fascists.'

'I wouldn't look for it if I were you.'

'Why not?'

'It's probably guarded by all sorts of occult forces.'

Gerald remained silent.

'You might meet the great white witch,' she said.

'I'm really into the idea,' said Robbie. 'I mean, Baba is the Avatar but this Christianity thing has a point,' he continued.

'So you're after it too. Well, I guess I might as well tag along. "The Knights of the Grail". Who'll be King Arthur? Norwald Thynne, I suppose, or Gerald. Gerald can be King Arthur. What do you reckon to that, Gerald?'

'Yes,' said Gerald.

'And we could all dress up in armour and I could give you each a rose.'

'I'll be Lancelot,' said Robbie.

'And I'll be Guinivere,' said Dianna.

'We'd have to ride horses,' said Robbie.

'I'll ride Jock,' said Dianna.

Robbie laughed. Gerald looked pained.

'What's the matter, Gerald, aren't we taking it seriously enough?' Dianna said.

'We've got to find the Holy Grail. Then all the fascists will drop dead,' said Gerald.

'That's a bit drastic, isn't it?' Robbie said.

'Not really,' said Gerald. He continued: 'I've been trying to paint a picture so good that all the forces of darkness will fall down dead. The Grail will do instead.'

'Oh, you're on about the forces of darkness still, are you?' said Dianna.

'Yes,' said Gerald.

'Seriously, Gerald, how are you going to start?' said Dianna.

'I'm going to ask a priest.'

'Yes, that makes sense.'

Dianna reached inside her bag and pulled out some sticks of incense. 'Can I stick one of these in a flowerpot, Gerald?' Gerald nodded. Dianna lit the joss stick and waved out the match. 'That'll cover up the smell of cats' piss,' she said.

Gerald grinned.

'Well, if I was going to look for the Grail I'd consult a medium, you know. They know everything,' Dianna said.

'Watch out, Dianna, you don't want to get into any more heavy scenes.'

'Oh, it's quite safe, Robbie. I went to one before to try and contact my grandfather. She was awfully nice. She gave me tea and cream cakes. We could go there again.'

'Where is it? I've never heard of there being a medium in York.'

'She's in Hope Street. She doesn't advertise. She doesn't want publicity.'

'How did you get to find her, then?'

'Oh, a man in a greengrocer's told me.'

'Well, it sounds a far out idea.'

'Not really. In the last century people used to do it all the time. You know, tables levitate, ectoplasm comes from people's mouths, people possessed with dead spirits, people's limbs lengthen.'

'Sounds fun.'

'Yes it is. My medium was quite ordinary, though. There was none of that happening. She was quite a homely sort of person really.'

'Does it cost much?'

'Well, it is rather expensive.'

'That rules that out.'

'Oh, we could all go together and it wouldn't cost so much.'

'Count me in, then.'

'Hey, Gerald, what do you think of that then?'

'Yes,' said Gerald.

'Hey, Gerald, make us a cup of coffee or something,' Robbie said.

Gerald fetched three cracked and chipped mugs out of the sink, one of which was painted with green oil paints. He put on a saucepan of water.

'Ask a priest, consult a medium. What have we got so far? What next?' said Dianna.

'I could ask Baba for advice,' said Robbie.

Three cats suddenly tumbled in through the door, sniffed hopefully at the plate on the floor and then prowled between the legs of the occupants of the kitchen.

'What are they called, Gerald? Oh!' said Dianna as a cat jumped on her lap and sank its claws in.

Gerald was a long time answering.

'Bovis, Lucy and Tiny,' said Gerald.

Robbie's hand snaked round from behind her and stroked it. Immediately another cat jumped up. The third cat was on the work surface by the cooker, but Gerald waved it off and it dropped adroitly to the floor, where it put up a hind leg and licked itself. They remained in silence for several minutes. The water in the saucepan boiled and Gerald poured out three cups of coffee. He handed them out. They sat drinking. Robbie had to tilt his head back to get enough room to insert the cup.

'Is Andrew into finding the Grail as well?' said Robbie.

'Andrew is a dictator,' said Gerald.

'Yes, but does he want to find the Grail?'

'Yes,' said Gerald.

'And Alec – have you asked Alec whether he'd like to be in on this?'

'No,' said Gerald.

'I'll go round and see him, then.'

'What about Chris?'

'Chris wants to.'

'And Mark?'

'Yes.'

'Right, that's nine of us. It should be enough if we're all looking.'

Chris Stricken, the poet, sat in his room. His room was a very bare room. The floorboards were bare and there wasn't much furniture. A table and chair was all there was. It was a pleasant enough room, though. The walls and ceilings were white, and the ceiling, being under the eaves, sloped down to meet the wall on either side of the room. A beam rose underneath the ceiling from one corner. There was a window and through this sunshine streamed, infusing the room with light. Outside the window was the platform of a fire escape, where people could sit and admire the view on a warm day. The room was heated by a paraffin stove. Chris was writing. A single sheet of paper was on the table. He had written:

The city is alive with worship
In its haze of heat and light
The orthodox dart
Threadbare in sequins
Electric through its murmurs.
The shadows are gorged with footsteps
And the pavements with shadows
The streets echo with song.

He paused, his biro lifted. He was tall and thin and his face was gaunt. His face, over which a mass of black curls sat, was scarred by some pain and suffering. He had not eaten for three days, unintentionally, as he had run out of money. He finished the poem in a scrawling script.

The faithful progress laughing
Through the heavy hectic facades
They conspire amongst and for.

He threw down the biro triumphantly, got up and paced around the room. He had to stoop, as the ceiling was too low. He was wearing a black leather jacket into which he stuck his hands. He whistled. He went to a cupboard and looked inside it. There was nothing but a few dry beans. He closed the cupboard gently.

Earlier that day he had managed to squeeze fifty pence out of Gerald. He had spent the money gambling on a horse, promising to win and pay Gerald back. Of course, the horse had lost and now neither he nor Gerald had any money, it having been Gerald's last fifty pence. Chris felt no conscience, though, as he knew that Gerald would find someone to get money off. The fact that these people in turn would be quite poor didn't bother Chris.

He went into the other room and threw himself on the cold bed. His flesh prickled with goose pimples. He brooded. He thought of poems in the shape of pears and apples or chickens, and considered eating his poetry. Lazily he considered the Grail. To find it seemed a fitting thing for a poet to do. He could write a poem about it, or an epic, journalising the progress of its seekers. He could be their cheerleader and inspire them on to greater efforts. He knew the story of the Grail, but in his version the Grail had been broken and fragments of it were dispersed around the world. For this reason he was less optimistic. Besides, he was so intent on writing that he didn't know if he could spare the time, especially for a quest which might take them abroad. His body grew colder and he pulled a blanket over himself. This was how he spent his days, either writing or on his bed or in search of food and money. However fruitless the quest might be, it supplied mystery to life and this he was all in favour of. There wasn't enough mystery in life. He did his best to supply mystery in his poetry, but a real-life mystery, that would be worth a lot. He imagined finding the Grail, and reflected on the quality of his own life. If he did find it, surely his luck would change. He could sell it for an enormous sum or charge pilgrims for a sight of it. Money. He wanted money. The occasional five pounds he got for a poem did little to keep him alive, nor did the occasional hour or so of washing up in a restaurant. With the fame he would get from discovering the Grail, surely his poems would begin to sell. Fame, riches: he smiled to himself at this impossible dream.

Andrew let himself into the house with the key he now had. Jock rushed through the half-open door, jumping and wagging his tail. Andrew ambled in. Mark was lying on the sofa with one eye cocked towards the door.

'Hello Mark. Are you alright?'

'Fine.'

'How did you get on with the professor?'

'Oh, OK. We had some ideas.'

'That's more that I did. I went to Gerald's and all he said was that I could join in as long as I kept my mouth shut.'

Mark laughed.

Andrew took off his waterproof and undid Jock's lead. He went to the sink whistling and washed his hands. 'What then?' he said.

'Well, there's a job for you, Andrew, when you go to Lindisfarne or Iona or Walsingham. You can make enquiries there.'

'Yes, I can do that, I think.'

'I'm going to ring all the people with the surname Graal, and I'm going to look up references at the British Museum.'

'Good. You're becoming a Christian already.'

'That'll be the day.'

'Sweet Jesus, I need a cup of tea,' said Andrew, turning on the kettle.

'You know,' he continued 'I'm getting hooked on this Grail idea.'

'Professor Thynne will write to some academics in Germany,' said Mark.

'I say! An international effort,' said Andrew, raising his eyebrows.

'Chris Stricken is interested too.'

'What, you mean that Chris who keeps taking money from Gerald? He writes very good poetry but he's a menace. He's an absolute rogue.'

Mark laughed. 'Well, you're not much better, you're always begging money from people,' he said good-humouredly.

'Yes, I suppose so. But I take it from people who can afford it, and I don't plead poverty and then go out and spend money on the cinema or the horses. I use it to survive.'

'Alright, Andrew.'

'Gerald's such a soft touch, you know. As I was walking back I passed Ivor the tramp heading in Gerald's direction. I'll swear he was after Gerald's money. He can't say no, Gerald, that's his trouble.'

'Ivor, yes. I've had dealings with Ivor. He used to know when Gerald got his money and stand waiting, ready to collect it. I caught him trying to sell Gerald a dozen eggs for a fiver. He'd probably taken the eggs from someone's doorstep as well.'

'Gerald gives money to tramps. We give Gerald money and then we have to get it off someone else and so it goes on. It almost makes me think that the poor are their own worst enemies. After all, they voted this damned government in. They're cutting their own throats. Maggie Thatcher should be shot.'

Mark grinned. 'The good old Christian anarchist, eh?'

'Yes, that's me.'

'Well, I think anarchy is the highest state a society can aspire to, but I'm worried that without the state the strongest will rule and give us even worse tyrants.'

'Yes, I'm afraid you're right, even though I've got a hankering after anarchy. Still, I don't do too badly myself. I've lived outside the tax laws, the social security, any form of authority, for years. And I don't want a thing to do with authority if I can help it.'

'Hoorah!' said Mark.

'No. I don't want to participate at all in this rotten society if I can help it. And you – you don't do too badly with your cleaning jobs and your marbling.'

'Yes. I've succeeded in living without a boss.'

'You know, riches seem to breed callousness. Some of my rich friends I go to are sitting on stacks of it, almost literally. They might slip me the odd fiver as a present but help, real help? Will they help? No they will not. They could easily afford to buy me a house and lift me right out of this mess. Very nice, very courteous, full of advice, but nothing of what really matters.'

'Bite the hand that feeds you.'

'Well, I must admit I'm reliant on them and grateful for what I get. But really!' Andrew tailed off. He went to the kettle and made a cup of tea. 'Ah, that's better,' he said, sipping it. He came back towards the sofa. 'What this country needs is a marvel. Something that will really make everybody sit and think. We've been to the moon. We may go to Mars. But humankind's spirituality is no better that it was a thousand years ago.'

'Things are better now.'

'Superficially, yes, but we live in a heartless age, an age of misery and drudgery, and loss of purpose. If we could find the Grail now, that would make the difference. It would make the old Protestant church jump. Quite honestly I think a lot of this relic business is a lot of mumbo jumbo, but if we could produce this one true relic, resplendent with radiant light and curing all those who touched it, then things would be different.'

'You might gain a lot of converts, but would the church really change? The church has always been on the side of oppression.'

'Rubbish. Or rather, it has made some pretty bad mistakes but fundamentally it is Good.'

'Your rich friends are churchgoers.'

'I'm afraid they are and there is a saying: "It is easier for a camel to pass through the eye of a needle than for a rich man to enter the Kingdom of God". And there's another one. Christ said to the rich man: "Sell all you have and give to the poor". Now, if people really took the message of the New Testament as it is written we'd see some changes. By golly we would.'

'If people were truly Christian they'd be socialists.'

'Something like that.'

'Professor Thynne told me that there were various conditions you have to meet before you could see the Grail.'

'Yes, you have to be chaste for one thing, which rules most of us out, but I really don't think God is going to exclude anybody from heaven simply because they loved someone.'

'I should hope not. Sex is God's gift as well, if there is a God.'

'Trouble is, we haven't got a Merlin the Magician to help us.'

'Gerald will do.'

Andrew laughed.

'And Dianna as Guinivere,' Mark said.

'I expect she's already thought of that.'

'What part can Jock play?'

'Oh, he's a regular Hell Hound, aren't you Jock?'

Jock looked upward enquiringly. There was a pause.

'Well, I must leave you tomorrow, you'll no doubt be glad to hear,' said Andrew.

'Where are you going?'

'North.'

'So you can go to Lindisfarne.'

'Yes. I think I will. And look here, I'll set off really early so that when you get up I won't be there. I'll try to make as little noise as possible and not wake you up. I must say I'm rather fed up of this existence, though, forever travelling around, but I'll tell you one thing, I'll be very glad to get out of York. I hate the town, the smelly roaring motor cars. I'm a country person at heart.'

'Will you see Gerald?'

'No, I don't think he particularly wants to see me at the moment, and anyway, I must make an early start. Do you still play the piano, Mark?'

'Not much.'

'You should, you know. You mustn't waste your talents. Whenever I think of you I think of Chopin. I always associate you two in my mind.'

'I'm flattered.'

'That Polonaise, whatever it is that goes *Da* Da Da Da di di didi *Da* Da Da.'

'Yes, I know the one, it's one of my favourites. But I couldn't play it now, I'm far too much out of practice.'

'Well, get in practice then.'

'I might.'

'I'd love to be able to play the piano. But I can pick out a few simple tunes and keep myself happy.'

'Yes, I know. That French-sounding tune.'

'That's right. Very simple but very pleasing.'

Mark sat upright and stroked his chin thoughtfully. 'It's started,' he said.

'What, may I ask?'

'The Hunt for the Grail. It's started. The first tentative moves have been made and soon it'll be in full swing.'

'Yes, Mark, it has.'

'I'm quite looking forward to it.'

'We're both looking forward to it.'

Robbie knocked on Alec's door. A few moments later Alec opened it.

'Hi, Alec.'

'Oh, hello Robbie, come in.'

Alec lead the way back to the main room along the gloomy corridor. They entered. On an armchair a massive mound of Chinese food steamed. Alec went over to it, sat down and started to eat furiously. Robbie sat down, opposite him.

'I've come to tell you that we're all going to look for the Holy Grail,' said Robbie.

Alec continued eating.

'I said we're all going to look for the Holy Grail,' Robbie repeated.

'Who?' Alec said absently.

'Me, Dianna, Mark, Andrew, Gerald, Chris, Tristan, Professor Thynne.'

Alec continued eating.

'We're going to have a séance.'

Alec continued eating.

'And I'm going to ask Baba about it.'

There was still no answer. Robbie gave up and slouched back in his chair. Minutes later Alec spoke. 'What's that, the Grail?'

Robbie explained again.

'Why do you want to find it?'

Robbie was silent, lost for an answer. Finally he spoke. 'Oh, it's just a far out idea, that's all.' He was silent again. 'Well, it's an adventure,' he said.

'Yes, I s'pose it is,' said Alec. 'Do you want some coffee without milk?'

he added. 'I've run out.'

'Yes thanks,' said Robbie.

'And I don't like the idea of holding a séance. That's rather dangerous, you know.'

'Why?'

'It's contrary to the church's teaching.'

'Oh, it'll be alright,' said Robbie.

'Anyway, loads of people have looked for the Grail.'

'How do you know?'

'A friend of mine used to be looking for it,' Alec said, as he left the room to prepare the coffee. There followed a great clanking and clattering as saucepans and plates fell to the floor. Minutes later he returned with two mugs.

'Did he have any luck?' said Robbie.

'It was a she. No, she had to be rescued from a pothole.'

'Alec, you're a real downer. I come here full of enthusiasm and you're so cool about it.'

Alec went to a corner and put on a tape of some music. 'It's certainly an unusual thing to do,' he said.

'I'll say it is.'

'And I suppose it would be quite wonderful to see it.'

'I think so too.'

'And it would be something to do.'

'Come on then, join us,' said Robbie, but Alec had gone into a trance. Moments later Alec very slowly turned his head towards Robbie.

'I'm not sure if God wants me to,' he said solemnly.

'God won't mind,' said Robbie.

Alec took out a bottle of cough mixture from his pocket and knocked back about half of it.

'What's the matter, Alec, have you got a cough?'

'No, I just like it, that's all. It's very warming. It helps me sleep. God may want to keep me for other things.'

'Oh yeah!'

'I've got a mission in life but I'm not sure what it is. It's yet to be revealed.'

'Haven't we all,' said Robbie. 'Well, while you're waiting for it to be revealed, why not come along with us?' he added.

'I'm not sure,' said Alec.

'Why not?'

'I'm not sure if my parents will approve. My father's a priest, you know.'

'Alec, you're in your thirties now, you can make up your own mind.'

'And I find Gerald and Norwald Thynne a bit too much, at least if I'm with them all the time.'

'Oh, they're alright. You know Professor Thynne said I was his intellectual equal. I'm quite proud of that.'

'Did he?' said Alec.

'Oh come on, Alec. It would be great to have you with us.'

'Well, I might.'

'I mean, let's face it – what do you do with your time?'

'I said I might.'

'Oh, alright. But think about it, then.'

'Yes, I'll think about it.'

'Lend us ten quid?' asked Robbie.

Somewhere in England or in the vast hinterland of the world was the Grail. Resplendent with light and an aura of holiness, it waited to be discovered, restless on its shrine or nestling in some forgotten cupboard. Little could its keepers know, basking in the glory of their secret, that its liberation and publication were being sought. But surely they guarded against this, jealously hiding their secret. Or perhaps some herdsman somewhere kept it on the mantelpiece of his cottage, unaware of its significance, but finding it a treasure in his life, warming his hands over it after a hard day's work in the open air. Could it have been melted down, and a gold ingot in a bank vault glowed with more than its allotted brilliance? Whatever the case, it was sought. It had already wrought a change in the lives of nine people and it would cause much greater change yet. Fictitious or not, it served to give additional purpose to the lives of the nine, and might suck yet more people into the dream of its brilliance. Knights in days of old might have prepared for the quest with prayer and fastings. In this day and age the preparations were different. There was a certain amount of praying, true, to various gods – some more arcane than others – but the preparations consisted mostly of rises in blood pressure and mental agitation, small celebrations here and there of the forthcoming events. Pictures were painted, poems were written, graffiti was sprayed on the walls of back streets. The dog and cats were possibly unaware of the excitement and continued to eat, sleep, and defecate quite naturally, unaware that they were liable to be transported long distances around the country or possibly abroad. Acquaintances of the nine thought that they detected changes in them, a greater thoughtfulness or silence. Could it be that the quest was already elevating them and giving them spiritual experience? Yet life continued much as normal, a few whispered conversations here, a despairing belly laugh there, an unobserved wondering and dreaming, much ranting at various points and the occasional roar. York was not shaken. It continued its daily round. Tourists came and went, motoring offences were committed. Dick Turpin turned in his grave once or twice. So far, the press had not got hold of the story, and a very garbled and confused story it would have been anyway. Besides, the local press were not especially interested in mystery; a more typical headline would have been: 'York man eats thirty pork pies.'

'Dianna,' said Mark.

'Yes Mark.'

'You couldn't do me a favour, could you?'

'Well, Mark…'

'Could you do my star chart for me?'

'You mean your birth chart?'

'Yes, that's it.'

'What's brought this on?'

'I want to find whether there's anything in my stars which suggests I'm cut out to find the Grail.'

'Oh, the Grail, is it? You're still serious about this?'

'Yes, fairly.'

'You shouldn't look at fate too much.'

'Well, you do all the time.'

'Yes, but I'm qualified for it.'

'Trust you!'

'Alright, Mark, I'll just get a pen and paper.' Dianna pulled at the bottom of a pile of rubbish. 'What's your birth date, Mark?' she asked.

'Ten one fifty six.'

'And your time of birth?'

'Er… Twelve fifteen p.m.'

'And where were you born?'

'Burton-on-Trent.'

'Right, that should be easy enough. Give me a week. I did Robbie's the other day. One of the things it said was that Robbie had heroic qualities.'

Mark laughed. 'Robbie's heroic? He's more of an anti-hero,' he said.

'And it said that he was spiritually advanced.'

'Well, there's all that Baba stuff.'

'I'm spiritually advanced.'

'Well now.'

'Yes. I contemplate that void. My mind's completely empty except for the void, nothingness.'

'That's just being empty-headed.'

Dianna laughed. 'You rotter, Mark,' she said.

'What are you doing about the Grail?' Mark said.

'Me? Well, I thought of having a séance.'

'A séance – I like it. When are you having it?'

'Well, not immediately. We've got to think of the right questions to ask the spirit, you know.'

'I see. Can I come too?'

'Yes, you can come.' There was a pause.

'Have you been to see Gerald recently?'

'Oh Gerald. He was on about Auschwitz again.'

Mark laughed.

'And he gave me a Mars bar,' she said.

'He gave me a tube of Smarties last time I went.'

'He goes all flirtatious when I'm there.'

'Poor Gerald.'

'Yes. I can handle it.'

'You don't suppose there's anything between him and Madeline, do you?'

'God, no. She told me I have to mind my manners and I wasn't brought up properly. The cheek.'

'Well, Dianna, you weren't brought up properly. Something went wrong.'

'Oh… you!'

Mark laughed. 'But it's a bit of a joke, Madeline talking about manners,' he added. 'You know Madeline once went for Andrew with a broken bottle?'

'No, but I can imagine it,' said Dianna.

'A broken whisky bottle for that matter.'

'She takes money off Gerald.'

'You can talk. I'd like to see the day when you pay back the money you've borrowed.'

'Oh Mark, I keep meaning to.'

Mark laughed.

Andrew had been on Holy Island for several days now, and at the moment we see him he was approaching it over the causeway. He had missed the tide and had had to wait for it to recede. He waded through the now shallow water with his shoes in one hand and his trousers rolled up, swaying slightly from side to side. Jock was with him, his large pink tongue lolling happily from his mouth.

Andrew sang to himself, an old song from the Music Hall. Pausing on a dry section of the road in the middle, he picked up a bundle of seaweed and dangled it in front of Jock. Jock growled and bit at the savage monster. Andrew had been quite happy these last few days. Away from the town and in a religious community he was in his element. And he had been made very welcome too, and given a feather filled bed to sleep in, in contrast to the hard floors he often had to put up with. He neared the village and as he did so, a car overtook him, the causeway now being clear for traffic. In the village he knocked on the door of a stone-built building and was admitted. In the hall where he disrobed was a glass dish with pebbles and seashells in it. Andrew bent over it, looking at their gleaming roundnesses. 'This is pretty,' he said.

He finished undressing and went into the living room. Here, about a dozen people sat, mostly reading newspapers. Some were visitors to the Island, pilgrims, and a smaller number were residents.

'Hello Andrew,' said an old man effusively.

'Hello John. I've just been to Alnwick to see the castle there.'

'Aye, it's a grand castle.'

'There's so much of it remaining. It was super. Though I can't say I cared much for that display of wealth in the rooms that were open. It's much nicer here, much more homely.'

'I'm the same way, Andrew. Give me a cottage with a coal fire and an old armchair any day.'

'Yes,' Andrew laughed approvingly.

'And how is that wee dog of yours enjoying his stay?'

'Jock? Oh he's enjoying it terribly. He goes hunting rabbits. Did you hear he caught one yesterday and Molly prepared it for supper?'

'You ate rabbit, then?'

'No. Jock's supper. I'm vegetarian.'

'A vegetarian.'

'The Bible says "Thou shalt not kill", and I take it literally. I can't help what Jock does, though; it would be unkind to feed him on vegetables.'

'Aye, a dog needs meat.'

'How's your new girl, Cilla, coming on?'

'Well, I wouldn't say it was easy. She's a bit strange, you know. A few nights ago there was a full moon and we found her dancing naked in the sea and singing to herself.'

'Oh dear. That's lunacy.'

'Aye, lunacy. It does happen.'

'Do you have many like Cilla?'

'No, she's the only one. Some of the others need a bit of looking after, though.'

'I suppose there's a limit to how many you can care for?'

'There is. Yes, there is. So many want to come here, though. We don't like having to turn folk away.'

'I've just come from York, John, and it's terribly weird down there. Your girl, Cilla, dancing in the sea would be quite normal in York.'

'It can't be as bad as all that, Andrew.'

'Well, I guess I've bumped into the underground of York's society. But it's different here. Even if people are a bit odd, it's somehow less squalid and more pleasant.'

'You like it here then, do you, Andrew?'

'Very much. Very much indeed.'

'And how long will you stay here, Andrew?'

'Frances says I can still till Friday.'

'Not so long, then?'

'It's enough. The Great Lord is good to me.'

'And then where are you off to?'

'I plan to go to Iona for a spell, to the community there.'

'It's a hard life you lead, Andrew.'

'Oh, it's not so bad. I have my downs but I get up again pretty quickly. My young friend Mark in York once said: "I think you have remarkable powers of recovery", and I think that the good Lord has indeed blessed me with that ability.'

'Aye, Andrew. You keep going. Things are bound to get better some day.'

'I'll turn atheist if they don't.'

John laughed. 'No. Not you, Andrew,' he said.

'You never know. Or perhaps I'll become Buddhist.'

'You stick to God and God won't let you down.'

A noise disturbed the conversation.

'Is that the supper gong?'

'Aye.'

The room emptied.

The next morning Andrew went to have a look at the castle. He sauntered up the winding path and up the steps to the entrance. He paid and went in. The castle was as homely as a cottage. All of its rooms were cottage-size rooms and there was no sign of adaptations for military purposes. From the rooms there was a good view of the Island, as the castle was on top of a small rocky hill. Andrew passed wistfully from room to room thinking how much he'd like to live there. As he'd intended, he stopped at the reception table on the way out and addressed the man there. 'Tell me, does Lindisfarne have any association with the Holy Grail?'

The man looked up, startled at being addressed. 'Holy Grail, now let me see. You're asking the wrong person really but I might think of something.' He paused. 'I think Arthur's country was further south. What makes you think that Lindisfarne'd have anything to do with it?'

'Well, I'm interested in where it went after the Knight Perceval found it.'

'I see. Well, I can't think of anything. I tell you what, though, you go and see old Percy Rider in the village. He's in the first house you come to as you go back.'

'Thank you so much for your help.'

Minutes later Andrew knocked on Percy's door.

'Grail! Who wants the Grail?' Percy shouted.

'Well, I've got this rather mad idea of finding it.'

'Humph. Well, you better come in.'

Andrew went in.

'So you want to know where the Grail is, do you? said Percy aggressively. 'I'll tell you where the Grail is. Satan snatched it and it's in Hell guarded by four fiery dragons.' Percy paced the room. 'Will you go to Hell? Will you?' he demanded. There was a pause. 'No, it's not in Hell,' he continued. 'But what if I told you where is was? What would you do then, eh? Like as not you'd use if for a porridge bowl.'

'You mean you know where the Grail is?' Andrew said respectfully.

'Know where the Grail is,' Percy repeated, savouring the words. He stopped moving and looked up dreamily. 'No,' he said quietly.

'Oh,' said Andrew.

'But my great grandfather would have known. My grandfather was a very fine man and I'll not hear you say otherwise,' he said, glaring at Andrew. 'By my beard, how do they make 'em these days?' He paused. 'It's a disgrace,' he said. Andrew didn't know what was a disgrace and kept quiet. 'Come with me,' he said urgently, tugging at Andrew's sleeve. Andrew followed him into another room. 'There, what do you think of that?' he said proudly. He gestured at a model ship on the mantelpiece, made entirely of seashells. 'That's better than any Grail.'

'You may be teaching me an important lesson,' said Andrew.

'If you want the Grail I can tell nothing. Nothing at all,' said Percy, and then looked down at his feet.

'Oh well, I'll leave you then.'

Percy saw him to the door. Back at the house Andrew had a talk with Frances.

'Frances, do you know if there are any legends on the island about the Holy Grail?'

'The Holy Grail. No, not that I can think of. In the archives there are bibles, an old chess manual written by a monk, a history of England, but I don't think there's anything of that sort.'

'Oh, that's a pity.'

'Why do you ask?'

'I want to find it.'

'Oh, jolly good, Andrew. How exciting.'

'Well, not yet, it isn't.'

'But what an eccentric thing to do.'

'Yes,' Andrew laughed.

'Are you looking by yourself?'

'No, there are some friends in York looking.'

'Well, you must keep me informed. I'd like to know if there are any developments.'

The next morning Andrew got up very early and set off to go further North. He was lucky with the tide this time and managed to get a lift to the A1 with a local woman. It was very cold and Andrew had on his usual layers of clothes. Jock was oblivious to the cold and happy to be on the move. His first lift was with a professional conjurer on his way to a performance, and Andrew swapped reminiscences with him as he had been on the stage himself. Andrew laughed. 'Do you know,' he said, 'when I was playing a pantomime I had to address Widow Twankey, a great bull of a man in woman's dress, and when it came to the line I said "Now Widow Wanky". The audience collapsed laughing and after that I was stuck with it. I couldn't say it any other way. I used to go bright red but I couldn't help it.'

The conjurer laughed appreciatively. They continued chatting happily and the conjurer offered Andrew a ham sandwich which Andrew was too polite to refuse. At Edinburgh it was time for another lift, and from here the hitching was slow. Andrew forged on wearily, and ended up hitching in the darkness.

Mark stood by the telephone waiting for his call to get through.

'Hello,' a voice said.

'Mr Graal?'

'Emmanuel Graal.'

'Mr Graal, I'm interested in your name.'

'What are you, the tax man or something?'

'No. I'm doing some research into the Holy Grail and Graal is the old way of writing Grail.'

'Grail – you think I might know something about it, then?'

'I'm hoping you do.'

'Well, as a matter of fact I do. There's an old story in our family that we once possessed it.'

'Oh, good. How long ago was that?'

'I don't rightly know. It may have been in the thirteenth century.'

'Where were your family living then?'

'I'm not sure, but the earliest Graals were based in Lancaster.'

'Do you know anything about the Grail itself?'

'Well, our story is that it was made of silver and studded with jewels, and it had some kind of writing on the inside rim.'

'Do you know anything else?'

'Well, the story goes that one of our ancestors lost it to pay for a gambling debt.'

'Do you know who to?'

'No, except that it was someone in the nobility.'

'Alright, thank you for your help.'

'Pleasure.'

Mark put the phone down. He rang another number.

'Grail – what is it?'

'Well, it's supposed to have contained Christ's blood.'

'How morbid.'

'And it's supposed to have been the chalice that Christ drank from at the Last Supper.'

'Are you suggesting that we might have had something to do with it?'

'Yes. I am.'

'How interesting. I always thought that our name was a bit funny.'

'You can't help me, then.'

'No.'

'Alright. Thanks. Goodbye.'

The next phone call was simple and to the point.

'F… off,' the voice said.

Mark put the phone down gently. He tried another.

'Yes, Martha Graal here.'

'I'm interested in your name.'

'Don't tell me you're looking for the Holy Grail.'

'Yes, that's right.'

'Well, I may be able to help you. It's not connected with our name, though. When my husband was in Singapore he overheard a conversation by some traders in town. They kept referring to 'the Grail' and there's no Singapore name like that. He thought they were talking about him at first, that's why it caught his attention, but then they referred to it as being worth its weight in diamonds. Naturally, my husband was interested. And he always wondered whether they had the Holy Grail. That's all I know, I'm afraid. I can't help you any more.'

'No. Thank you, that's a great help. Goodbye.'

Mark jotted down notes on a writing pad he had handy.

'Hello, Doctor Graal?'

'Doctor Graal speaking.'

'I'm doing some research into the Holy Grail or Graal. I wondered if you have any old stories in your family.'

'Well, there is. The founding member of our family is supposed to have taken his name from being one of the Knights of King Arthur. I've always thought that a bit fanciful myself. After all, no-one's established that King Arthur ever existed.'

'Do you know anything about that founding member?'

'No, nothing at all, I'm afraid.'

'Well, thanks for your help.'

'I'm quite interested in the Grail legend myself. I'd be much obliged if you could ring me if you find out anything important.'

'Yes, I could do that. Thanks again. Goodbye.'

Mark tried another number.

'Hello. Eusebius Graal here.'

'I'm doing some research into the Holy Grail or Graal and I wondered if you have any stories in your family.'

'What is the Graal?'

'A holy relic that was pursued by the Knights of King Arthur.'

'Well, you've got the wrong person. I'm West Indian.'

'Oh,' said Mark.

'Knights of King Arthur. Wow!' said Eusebius, laughing.

'They really did exist,' said Mark.

'I don't doubt it, man. That sounds like a far out trip.'

'Yes.'

'No, don't ask me.'

'Well, goodbye then.'

Gerald scurried along the street keeping close to the wall. He walked in this way because he'd once nearly been hit by a lorry and so now, if someone were to walk on the inside of him, Gerald would dodge round them, trying to get further away from the traffic. He was wearing white gloves and a white coat from which his frilly blouse peeped. Covering his eyes was a black paper mask and his lips were painted bright red. In his left hand he carried a cat in a basket which was quite docile, being used to being carried around in this way. Gerald turned into the drive of a large house, and knocked on a large black door.

'Yes,' said the priest on opening it.

'Tell me where the Holy Grail is or I'll shoot you,' Gerald said, pointing his gun at him. The priest regarded Gerald benignly. Gerald's hand began to tremble. 'Bang,' went the gun.

The priest still looked on benignly. 'Would you like to come in?' he said.

'Yes,' said Gerald.

He crossed himself as he went inside. He was led into a spacious sitting room where a coal fire blazed. 'Sit down. Yes, that's right, by the fire,' said the priest.

Gerald sat down and looked at his feet. 'Can I let Lucy out?' he said.

'By all means.'

Gerald unstrapped the basket and Lucy jumped out. Promptly she went to a corner of the room and defecated.

'Oh dear,' said the priest, looking aghast.

'Sorry,' said Gerald.

'Now then,' said the priest, settling into an armchair opposite Gerald. 'You must be very desperate to find the Holy Grail if you're prepared to shoot me for it,' he said, beaming. Gerald remained silent. 'How can I help you?' he mused.

'All I want to know is where the Grail is,' said Gerald.

'Well, seek and ye shall find.' Gerald looked up attentively. 'It's rather hard for me to answer. I've never had a request of this sort,' the priest added. 'I have the feeling you need healing. Why do you need the Grail? If you were filled with the Holy Spirit you wouldn't need the Grail.'

'Yes, but tell me where the Grail is,' said Gerald.

'It may be in Timbuktu for all I know. I really don't know, I'm afraid.'

'Someone's got to know,' said Gerald.

'Perhaps there is, indeed, someone somewhere who can help you.'

Gerald fumbled inside his coat and brought out a piece of paper which he handed to the priest. The priest read:

The light again merges and, so with all comparison brought, Noah's ark, and his Creatures. Birds, leopards, snakes, lizards, swans, horses etc. If only the joy in the heart was felt. Then the Truth has, light enough to strive. In many corners. To shine through the trees and makes the sap green leaves glow almost radiant hue. The whole of nature is with colour. For creation is like a budding flower. The earth revolves and keeps revolving in heaven's power. For God is the judge, the force which controls the love which is so for the pity. To pity. Which the afflicted in knowledge of right. The wondrous truth shines around…

'Yes, you are truly a child of God,' said the priest, handing back the paper to Gerald. 'But I read pain in these sentences.'

'I'm alright, but other people won't leave me alone.'

'You are harassed by other people?'

'Yes.'

'Tell me more.'

'Norwald Thynne practices black magic on me.'

'That is bad. However, I can teach you a remedy. Stand up. What is your name?'

'Gerald.'

'Well, stand up Gerald.'

Gerald stood up. Lucy tried to climb up his leg.

'Face East. No, the other way. The magnetic current we propose to use runs from East to West. Now you must steady your own vibrations and purify your aura. Touch your forehead. Now say "To thee O God". Touch your solar plexus, that's it. Now say "Be the Kingdom". Touch your right shoulder. Now say "And the Glory". Now clasp your hands and say "Unto the ages of the ages. Amen". By this formula you affirm the power of God as sole creator and supreme law of the universe to which all things must bow. Next Gerald, imagine that you clasp in your right a two-handed sword. Hold it point upward and say, "In the name of God I take in hand the Sword of Power for defence against evil and aggression". Gerald, imagine yourself towering up to twice your natural height, dressed in mail, and vibrating with the force of the Power of God with which you have been charged by your formulation of the Sword of Power. Now, Gerald, draw a circle on the floor around yourself. You must imagine a line of flames following the line of the sword. Draw it clockwise. Yes, that's right. Now cease visualising the sword, but, still seeing the circle, clasp your hands and raise them above your head, facing East again. Say "May the mighty Archangel Raphael protect me from all evil approaching from the East". Turn to the South. No, the other way. Now invoke Michael in the same way. West, invoke Gabriel. You're doing well. North, invoke Uriel. Turn East. Now repeat the cross you started with. How do you feel now, Gerald?' There was no answer. 'Gerald?'

Gerald had turned as white as a sheet and was shaking slightly.

'Oh Gerald, don't worry. It's God's magic, not the Devil's. Now do you think you can remember all of that?'

'Yes,' said Gerald, sinking back into the chair and rubbing the sweat on his forehead.

'You see, I know a thing or two they didn't teach in theological college. Norwald Thynne won't bother you any more. Have you any other troubles?'

'No,' said Gerald hurriedly.

'Would you like some tea and biscuits after that ordeal?'

'Yes please.'

The priest went to make the tea and Gerald remained rubbing his forehead. By this time Lucy was halfway up the curtains and looking certain to reach the top. After a minute Gerald left the chair and crouched in front of the fire, turning his hands to warm them. The room was sumptuous by Gerald's standards. A glass chandelier hung down in the centre of the room. The curtains on which Lucy climbed were velvet. The rug looked as if it might have come from the Middle East. All the woodwork, including the bookcase and table, was of teak. Pictures lined the walls in heavy gold frames, pictures that were almost certainly originals, although they were mostly sentimental Victorian works of, for example, a shepherdess in a bonnet with a blue ribbon and a crook, with an impossibly clean sheep next to her. Over the mantelpiece was a mirror also framed in gold, with small cherubs carved at its corners. A large elaborately bound Bible sat on the table.

The priest returned with a silver teapot on a tray and some fine porcelain cups. He poured out the tea and offered Gerald a biscuit. Gerald accepted and sat back in the chair. 'Can you lend me a pound?' he said.

The priest frowned, but then said smiling, 'I can give you a pound.' He brought out his wallet and handed Gerald the pound.

'Blessed are the poor for they shall inherit the earth,' said Gerald.

'Certainly,' said the priest.

'It says that in the Bible.'

'Indeed.'

'Why are you so posh and stuck up?'

The priest looked at Gerald, startled. 'Well, the good Lord has blessed me with good fortune.'

'There's too much hypocrisy.'

'There is indeed, Gerald.'

'There's too much hypocrisy. You live in luxury but tell everybody else to be poor.'

'Not quite, Gerald.'

'Would you let me live here?'

'No Gerald. I have a wife and family and there would be no room for you, I'm afraid.'

'Well then.'

'Well what?'

'You won't let me stay here because I'm poor and I've got a gun.' Gerald took out the gun and fondled it menacingly.

'No Gerald, I've told you why you can't live here.'

'If you hate me so much, why don't you get a knife and slit my throat?'

'I don't hate you, Gerald. I like you. You're an unusual little fellow.'

Gerald interrupted. 'Go on, get a knife and go for me. I've had that happen to me before now.'

'Poor Gerald.'

'I come to you looking for help and all you can do is say "Poor Gerald".'

'I've done more than that.'

'Not much. The church doesn't know what God is. The church is corrupt.'

'Now steady on, Gerald.'

'The church is pompous and stuck up. All those women in their flowery hats and men in suits.'

'We all worship God in our own way.'

'Well, some ways are better than others.'

'How do you worship, Gerald?' Gerald was silent. 'Are you looking for the Grail on your own?' said the priest.

'Yes.'

'All by yourself,' the priest mused.

'Well, there are some other people,' Gerald conceded.

'How many?'

'I'm not sure, about thirty.'

'Well, well, the things that go on. I'm surprised I hadn't heard of this before. And how are you getting on? Have you found any of the threads to the centre of the web?'

'No,' said Gerald.

'Well, keep searching, and if you find it, bring it to me. I could place it in a shrine in my church.'

'So that's what you're up to?'

'Of course, the glory would be yours, but the true glory would be God's.'

'Opportunism.'

'Well, what would you do with it, Gerald? It must be available to the public. This great wonder must be shared. But look, it's been lost for over a thousand years, how can you hope to find it?'

'We'll find it,' said Gerald doggedly.

Mark was round at Dianna's. He sat on a stack of old magazines.

'The ascendant of the chart, the sign rising over the eastern horizon at the time of birth, is Taurus. The sun is in Capricorn. In your chart the Capricorn qualities of reliability, caution and ambition are more dominant, though these may be modified by Taurean stubbornness and laziness at times. The seventh house is emphasised in your chart due to the conjunction of Saturn and Mars. This house rules close relationships. Scorpio is on the cusp and can give an indication of a marriage partner. Mars, being in its own sign, suggests deep emotions which should be allowed to flow freely. The sex drive is strong and needs expression…'

'I haven't noticed,' said Mark.

'Saturn trine to Uranus emphasises will power, and gives an insight into the workings of the universe; perhaps Yoga, astrology or the occult

may interest you. Aquarius on the cusp suggests you are more likely to
benefit from working in groups…'

'Well, I am working in a group.'

'The sixth house rules work and subordinates, and health. Here you
have Neptune which warns against laziness or lack of concentration in
the work sphere. There is also a suggestion to watch out for drugs.'

'I'm always watching out for drugs.'

'The eighth house rules sex, death and the occult, and inheritances.
The moon in this house gives preoccupation with death and the afterlife
and lends itself to research into psychic matters.'

'Now that's more like it.'

'The ninth house has Capricorn on the cusp. This gives a restricted
materialistic attitude to the qualities ruled by this house of higher education and long distance travel. Religious and philosophical attitudes may
be rigid.'

'I like that!' Mark said indignantly.

'The trine of the sun to the ascendant gives great energy, self-confi-
dence, and a positive outlook, especially in co-operation with others. The
Midheaven conjunct, the sun, means there should be influence through
your career in such areas as psychology and spirituality. The third house
suggests you may be nervous and highly-strung, with high ideals that lack
practical outlet, although there is an emphasis on mediumistic and occult
matters in your chart, and this may be a source of trouble to you. There is
a strong emphasis that you should cope with any inharmonious conditions on these levels.'

'The occult sure has been a trouble to me,' said Mark.

'And that's that,' said Dianna. 'I've written it out. Do you want to take
it away and look at it?' she added.

'Yes, I might as well.'

'Well, what do you think?'

'Thanks very much, Dianna. I can't quite judge from that whether I'll
make a good Knight of the Grail. "Pre-occupation with the occult" maybe
suggests it, and I like the idea that I'd be good at coping with the occult.
How did you learn to do this, Dianna?'

'Oh, a Tibetan monk taught me.'

'A Tibetan monk!'

'Yes. I met him watching TV at Alec's once and he said, "Come with
me girl and I will introduce you to some mysteries".' She mimicked the
monk's voice.

'That's an original way of picking someone up.'

'No, he wasn't like that. He was awfully nice. He had a close-cropped head like a hedgehog and he was wearing long robes. His voice was ever so deep. Have you ever heard records of monks chanting, a sort of rumbling sound? Well, it was just like that.'

Robbie stood in the living room of his house. He stood centrally with his arms hanging loosely by his sides, his head resting on his chest. He stood that way for several minutes, then turned around slowly and walked towards the couch. This was Robbie's place of prayer. He stretched out on it comfortably, his legs hanging over the end of it. He began by intoning the name of Baba silently, but after a few minutes, stopped.

'Baba, do you know where the Grail is?' he asked in his thoughts. There was no answer.

'Be a sport, Baba.'

There was no answer.

'I mean, you are the avatar, you know everything.'

There was no answer.

'I mean it would be really far out to find the Grail.'

Robbie lay silently for a few more minutes.

'If you won't tell me, I won't worship you any more.'

Silence.

'I'm warning you.'

Silence.

'Oh Baba, go on.'

Silence.

'Baba?'

Silence.

'Oh hell,' Robbie said.

Tristan was in Bradford where he had returned after his fortnightly visit to the professor. He had told his ageing mother what was afoot and she had responded with ooha and ohs, urging him, however, to keep warm, wear an extra pullover and not to get into trouble with the police. Now he was in the streets of Bradford, as he had been all of the days of that week, visiting antique and junk shops. He entered a particularly dingy and litter-strewn street called 'Prawn Street' and stopped in front of a shop with the name 'Papadopulis' written over it. He looked in through the tear-stained window. Inside were many objects which gleamed, and this gave Tristan hope. There were objects of glass and brass, chrome, and piles of interesting looking boxes. He went inside. The owner stood in the gloom at the rear of the shop, rubbing his hands and wearing a woollen hat.

'Good morning,' said Tristan.

'Morning,' said Mr Papadopulis.

Tristan looked around him and saw a pair of chest expanders. He picked them up and stretched them across his chest.

'Eight quid those are,' said Mr Papadopulis.

Tristan continued exercising.

'Here, they'll only be worth a fiver by the time you've finished with them,' Mr Papadopulis said good-humouredly.

Tristan stopped, breathing hard. 'I think I'd like to buy these,' he said.

'You do that, sir. Though I must say you don't look the physical sort.'

'I'd like to be,' said Tristan.

Tristan carried the expanders reverentially to the owner and paid for them. Mr Papadopulis, put in a good humour by the sale, ventured a comment. 'Cold, innit?'

'Oh, it's bitter,' said Tristan.

'You from round here?'

'Yes, I was born in Bradford,' Tristan said proudly.

'You look more the southern sort if I may say so.'

'No. Bradford. Bradford's best.'

'I'll say it is,' said Mr Papadopulis respectfully.

Tristan browsed around the shop for a further time then addressed Mr Papadopulis. 'Have you got the Holy Grail in stock?'

'Bound to have, you just keep looking.'

Tristan wandered over to a corner of the shop. 'Is this it?' he said, holding up a brass chalice.

'It might be,' said Mr Papadopulis encouragingly.

Tristan went over to the window with the object and turned it over in the light. On its side was the inscription: 'Wheatfields one hundred yards P. Snace'. Tristan frowned.

Could the Grail have been used as a school running cup? It was possible. Tristan spun it round in his hands and wondered. He put it down, stood back and looked at it, then picked it up again. He took it to the rear of the shop.

'Well, if it was a school running cup, I'd ask you two pounds for it. But as it's the Holy Grail I'll ask you one pound,' said Mr Papadopulis.

Tristan paid. 'You don't know where it came from, do you?' he said.

'Well, if I remember rightly, an old fellow brought it in. He'd won it when he was young but he was a bit hard up.'

So it might be at least fifty years old. This added to the likelihood that it might indeed be the Grail. Tristan clutched the chalice tightly and left the shop. He walked along the road humming gently to himself, one hand engaged with the grip of the chest expanders. The professor would be pleased. He entered a larger street, studying the shops as he passed them. He stopped in front of a large antiques shop and went in. A man in a black suit and tie, with a neat parting in his hair, greeted him.

'Excuse me, but have you got the Holy Grail here?' Tristan asked humbly.

'We don't stock holy relics.'

'Oh, I'm sorry. Why not?'

'It's our policy. Anyway, I don't believe in them, they're a fraud.'

'This one isn't.'

'Well, you must look elsewhere, sir. Why don't you try Bewletts the hardware store?'

'Oh, thank you.'

Tristan left the shop humming and turned back into the side streets. Minutes later, he stopped stock still. On the window of a small shop in big capital letters were the words 'Holy Relics'. He went in.

'Can I help you?' the shopkeeper asked.

'I want a holy relic,' said Tristan.

'Well, you've come to the right place. I can offer you pieces of the true cross. They're the most expensive. Christ's jaw bone. The left shoe of Saint Mario the Blue, the hair of Pope Justin the First, who practised black magic. The tooth of Teresa of Avila. What do you want?'

'I want the Holy Grail please.'

'Holy Grail is it, well now,' said the shopkeeper, stroking his beard. 'They come rather pricey and I'm not sure if we have one in stock.'

'Oh please,' said Tristan.

'Sure you won't take St. John's shin bone instead?'

'No, it's the Grail I want.'

'Oh well then, wait a minute and I'll see,' said the shopkeeper, disappearing into the rear of the shop. He returned a moment later with a pewter chalice.

'I thought it was made of gold,' said Tristan.

'This one's made of pewter.'

'You're sure it's a true relic?'

'Yes certainly, you can see the maker's name engraved on the bottom.'
Tristan eyed it doubtfully.
'This one's twelve quid,' the shopkeeper said.
'Haven't you got any others?' said Tristan.
'No, this is the only one. You should have come last month, we had a lovely brass one with glass gems stuck into it.'
'Oh, that's a pity,' said Tristan.
'Go on, take it. We may never have another.'
'Oh, I'll take it.'
'Good. I knew you would. Holy Grails aren't so easy to find these days. Shall I wrap it up for you?'
'Yes please.'
The shopkeeper wrapped it up in tissue paper and put it into a box which he handed to Tristan. 'You won't regret it, I assure you. It will give you many hours of pleasure.'
Tristan left the shop. He wasn't entirely convinced that he had found the true Grail and so he continued looking. He found a junk shop in Ukulele Street which looked a likely place.
'Holy Grail, why not? We have everything here.'
'Oh good, could you show me it?'
'You'll have to look yourself. I'm not sure what we've got in the shop.'
Tristan browsed amongst the items on display. There was a stuffed fox and stuffed owl, numerous tables and chairs, piles of seventy-eight records and many more things. He rooted through one particularly densely cluttered corner. 'Oh what's this?' he said, removing a strange-looking metal device.
'God knows,' said the owner.
Tristan pressed a button on it and a metal rod sprang out and punched him on the nose. 'Oo! I don't think much of that,' he said, replacing it. He came upon a feather duster. 'How much is this?' he queried.
'Oh, fifty pence.'
He paid for it. He would use it to dust the professor's books. At last he came upon what he was looking for, another brass chalice. He held it aloft proudly.
'Is that what you were looking for?' said the shop owner.
'I think so.'
'It looks like a brass cup to me.'
'No, it's a chalice and it's made of gold.'
'No, it's not, it's brass.'
'I don't think so.'

'Well, if it's gold I'll charge you ten pounds instead of five.'

'That's more expensive that the last one I bought.'

'Ten pounds it is.'

Tristan looked in his purse. His funds were depleted. He continued his search until five o'clock and then came home.

'What a lot of Grails you've got!' said his mother looking at the collection which Tristan had spread out on the mantelpiece. Amongst them was a plastic Grail.

'Christ may have used more than one,' said Tristan. 'Or perhaps I've got the ones which his disciples used as well. I must ask Norwald.'

'Well, they're all very nice dear,' said his mother, flicking a duster over them. 'Yes, you be a good boy and take them to the professor. I'm sure he'll be pleased.'

Tristan, who was in his fifties, took this without comment. 'I want to paint a picture with you in front of them, mother,' he said.

'Oo, Tristan,' said mother.

'I want to do it to inspire everybody.'

'You do that, Tristan.'

Mark was busy on an errand of his own. He walked through town and into Coney Street. Near the end of the street he turned and entered a building. This was the office of the *Evening Press*, York's daily newspaper. He approached the counter and joined the queue. 'I want to place an advertisement.'

'Under which heading?'

'Uh, Personal, I suppose.'

'What is it, then?'

'Witch, Wizard or practiser of distant influence wanted for help in a good cause.'

The woman behind the counter regarded him suspiciously. 'Why do you want a wizard?' she said in a hostile voice.

Mark paused for a moment. 'I want some help with something I've got into.'

'Just a moment. I'll see if we can allow it.' She went off and conferred with a colleague. Mark heard the word 'Nutter' being used. She came back.

'I don't know whether we can allow this. The *Evening Press* is a reputable paper, you know. I think I'll have to give this to the manager to look at overnight.'

Mark left the building and wandered around. He suddenly changed his mind and went back to the office. 'I've changed my mind about the advert. I might get some really unpleasant people answering it.'

'You don't want it, then?'

'No, but you'd be surprised at the things that go on.'

'Yes,' said the woman, humouring him.

Andrew approached the Island of Iona. He was in a boat and he looked down at the sea over the side. The water was so clear that he could see to the bottom of it, the seabed. He reflected that life wasn't bad. A part of him was exhausted by this constant journeying but another part, uppermost in his mind at this moment, was excited by travel and the arriving at places. The boat nosed into the small harbour of Iona. Andrew got out with Jock. Soon he was wandering around the precincts of monastic settlement. Half an hour later, as he rounded a corner, he nearly bumped into a massively built man. 'Sorry,' he said.

'Well now?' said the man.

'Nice day,' said Andrew.

'What's your game?' said the man, eyeing Andrew sternly.

'I'm a visitor to the community and I hope I'll be put up here for a while.'

'I've been watching you,' said the man menacingly.

'Oh, really.'

'You've been buzzing around like a blue-arsed fly.'

'Just looking.'

'Looking, eh? Not a crime. Not a crime.'

'I hope not.'

'So you're going to be staying here?'

'I hope so.'

'You're a fine pillock. Want to stay with us, as if we haven't got enough scum staying here.'

'You're a monk then,' Andrew said doubtfully.

'A monk. By God, I'm a monk.'

'I don't think I've met you before.'

'I'm the King of the scum.'

'Oh.'

'Yes, I look after them and mother them. I'll look after you too if you don't watch it, pillock.'

'My name is Andrew Feather,' Andrew said.

'Feather, eh! You won't get any feathers with us. I'll call you Robin Hood.'

'If you must.'

'Yes, I must,' said the monk regretfully.

'I've got another reason for coming,' said Andrew.

'Stone me, whatever next?'

'I'm interested in finding the Holy Grail.'

'That's a tricky one.'

'Yes, the Holy Grail, radiant with holy light,' said Andrew brightly.

'Bright as a button on a sweep's arse,' the monk said ruminatively.

'Er, yes,' said Andrew.

'Bright as a button on a sweep's arse on a frosty morning. It would be a grand sight.'

'I think so.'

'What are your qualifications?'

'Qualifications?'

'Yes, you've got to have qualifications to find the Grail. Take me, I'm highly qualified.'

'Oh, how are you qualified?'

'King of the scum. Custodian of the bells. Scourge of the refectory. And I know Pythagoras.'

'Pythagoras?'

'The square on the hypotenuse is equal to the sum of the squares on the other two sides. I've had a classical training, you see.'

'I see. Well all I can call myself is a sort of middle-aged bum.'

'Bum! I'll say you're a bum. You look a hundred percent bum to me. Nothing wrong with a bum, though. Some of them are quite pretty. I've seen many bums in my time.'

'Well, a traveller.'

'Traveller. You've changed your mind have you? I'll tell you what you really are. You're a lamb, a fine frisky lamb.'

'Oh really,' said Andrew smiling.

'And if you don't watch it, I'll make mutton chops of you.'

'I don't know what to say to that.'

'They generally don't. I've got them foxed.'

'Tell me, though, do you know anything about the Grail?'

'Do you know anything about rats? The place is swarming with them. If I have my way I'll lasso them, mash them with turnips and feed them to the pigs.'

'Ugh!' exclaimed Andrew.

'Little devils,' the monk said admiringly.

'What you need is another Pied Piper.'

'Pied Piper – nonsense! I'd go for them with my teeth if only the Abbot would let me. There's no use messing around with the rats.'

'No, I suppose not.'

'Take my father, for instance, he used to eat rat pie on a Wednesday night. Lovely it was, almost as good as beef.'

'I don't believe you.'

'We were so poor, that was the only meat there was.'

'I still don't believe you.'

'You may be onto something there – but poverty's given me a grand training for life. I mean, look at me now. Look at me!' the monk demanded. Andrew looked at him. 'That's better. I like being looked at. Some folks can't stand it, but me, I like being looked at.'

'So you can't help me with the Grail.'

'I only wish I could. By the way, you mustn't mind me too much. My name's Joe.'

'You couldn't show me to a room, could you?'

'Poor lamb. Yes, I'll take you there. Are you hungry?'

'Well, I am a bit.'

'Never mind, there's a roast dog in the oven,' said the monk, slapping Andrew heartily on the back.

'I hope not,' said Andrew.

'Aye, a roast dog and a very fine one too.'

The monk put his hand paternally on Andrew's shoulder and steered him towards the entrance. It was mealtime in the refectory and Joe took Andrew straight there. He introduced Andrew to a monk by whom there was a spare chair. 'This is Robin Hood. Wants to find the Grail. Pillock.'

'Be seated, brother,' said the new monk courteously.

'Brother!' Joe muttered to himself, moving away.

Andrew slept well that night, and in the morning went for a walk around the island. He walked along by the sea with Jock, admiring the red stones of the Iona beaches and not thinking of anything in particular. He walked a long way, missing out on lunch at the monastery. He was in high spirits, and occasionally sang to himself. On a sandy stretch of beach he paused and inspected the sand. Many seashells protruded from it, tinged with pink or green. Andrew filled his pocket with them and passed on. He had a chat with a farming type, and another with an old woman who was putting her washing out. He wasn't too dispirited in his lack of success in tracing the Grail. For him, the quest was incidental to his life and served more as a diversion from the monotonous round of travel. He would make further enquiries, though.

Later that day he was introduced to the Abbot. 'Sylvester, may I ask you a question?' he asked, when they had completed the routine civilities.

'Yes Andrew, certainly.'

'Have there been any connections between Iona and the Holy Grail?'

'Why do you ask?'

'I'm interested.'

'As a matter of fact, there is. There's an old story that it was brought here for safe keeping at the time of the Norman conquest.'

'Have you any idea what happened to it after that?'

'The story is rather garbled, but one indication is that it may have been taken to France. Another is that the monks thought it too dangerous to be in possession of such a holy relic and buried it somewhere.'

'You've no idea where?'

'No, Andrew, that is all I know. What motivates your interest?' said the Abbot, after a pause.

'Well, I'm slightly embarrassed to mention it really. It seems so silly, but I'd like to find it.'

'For yourself?'

'For the world and for my friend Mark who might be persuaded by it to take up Christianity.'

'So it's not entirely selfish?'

'No.'

'Well, God bless you then. We will say a prayer for you tomorrow morning.'

Andrew bowed and left the Abbot's presence. Thanks to Joe, word had spread amongst the monks that Andrew was looking for the Holy Grail and in the refectory that evening there was competition as to who should sit next to him.

'Andrew, if I may call you that, what's this about the Grail?'

'Oh nothing really, it's just something I'd like to find.'

'You realise that it would be worth a lot of money?'

'Yes, priceless.'

'Priceless yes. And what would you do with it if you found it?'

'I hadn't really thought about it.'

'You should give it to us you know and we could sell it to Rome. We always need funds here.'

'Well, maybe.'

'If I were to give you five hundred pounds, would you give it to me?'

'What are you suggesting?'

'Five hundred pounds. Think what you could do with that.'

'I've never possessed more than ten.'

'Well then.'

'No, the Grail must be given to society as a whole.'

'Phooey! They wouldn't know what to do with it.'

'You underestimate people.'

'I've had enough to do with people, that's why I came here.'

'Oh yes?'

'Yes. They gave me ten years for armed robbery. And when I came out I said to myself, I'm never going to risk that again. I'm going to do it the legal way. I get free food, free clothes and company here, and if prayers are a bit boring I can always think of my girlfriend.'

'You've got a girlfriend?'

'Yes. I go absent without leave every now and then.'

'Does the Abbot know?'

'The old coot. I shouldn't think so.'

'Do you know Joe?'

'Joe, yes, he's a good sort once you get to know him. He got thrown out of the army for insubordination.'

'Another male institution, then.'

'That's right. He can't stand women. If you'll give me the Grail I'll let you live in my house.'

'You've got a house?'

'Of course. You can't have a girlfriend without having a house. We have parties there. You'd like it. Parties! I can give you five hundred because I've got money in stocks and shares.'

'Stocks and shares?'

'Yes. They never traced the money that I got through crime.'

'You're most unlike my idea of a monk.'

'You should talk to Peter. He got done for GBH but they let him off on a technicality. He's a good sort, too.'

'Are there any honest monks here?'

'A few, but we don't like them. Stuck up bastards. On about God all the time.'

Gerald was sitting in the kitchen of his flat. The cats played around him. His legs were crossed and the uppermost leg swung back and forth. He looked towards the far work surface; beside the plant pots there was a plastic dinosaur, painted in yellow and greens. It was this that he looked at. He regarded it steadily for a long time. After that time he got up, left the room and came back with a picture. The picture was in oils and was an idyllic bathing scene set around a pool in a forest with mountains in the background. He picked up a brush, a tube of oil paint and a piece of broken glass which served as a palette. Slowly, meticulously, he painted in the dinosaur amongst the bathers.

Manfred enjoyed his job. Dusting the books of the British Museum was a gentle and relaxing occupation. He had come to know many books by their titles and authors and had his favourites over which he lingered, taking more than his usual care. He liked the atmosphere of reverence for learning, and the silence, broken only by the rustle of pages. The visitors here were an interesting crowd as well. There were many eccentrics, and men with long white beards who could have come from the last century. Occasionally Manfred was dissatisfied with his job. There was one job which he had considered with envy ever since starting at the Museum. This was the job of the 'Chewing-gum man', whose chore it was to wander around the museum all day with a scraper, removing chewing-gum from the floor and under ledges. Manfred was in the cleaners' den where the cleaners would sit with a cup of coffee and smoke. Ned and Paul were in the room with him.

'Ned, watch your coffee, you're spilling it,' said Paul.

'It's alright, the museum pays for it,' said Ned.

'Museum pays to have your trousers cleaned as well,' said Paul.

'Praised be the museum,' said Ned.

'Yeah, it's amazing what you can get out of the old place. When they were having some new shelves put up, I got hold of a load of aluminium and sold it for scrap,' said Paul.

'Not bad,' said Ned.

'And when they get a glass door stove in, there's only a part of it smashed. I come in with my glass cutter and Bob's yer uncle, I've got a new window for nothing,' said Paul.

'Good on you!' said Ned.

'Yes, always got my eyes skinned,' said Paul.

'Do you remember that time when the Sultan of Arabia, whatever he was, came and gave us a gold piece each?' said Ned.

'Yeah, I've still got mine,' said Paul.

'Hey Manfred, stop reading that posh newspaper and talk with us,' said Ned.

Manfred put down his newspaper and smiled. 'Posh? It's only the Guardian,' he said.

'Can't read it myself. Tried once but I couldn't get past the front page,' said Ned.

'You intellectual Kraut you,' said Paul.

'Nein, ich bin Englander,' said Manfred.

'There we go again,' said Ned. 'We beat you in the last war, but up you come again, and now you're even taking our jobs,' he continued. 'Anyway, you've never told us what you're doing working here. You should have stayed as a sculptor like you said you once was. What did you say you did, now? Smash your sculpture with a hammer and walk out of school, something nutty like that.'

'Yes, I did truly,' said Manfred.

'And now you've ended up here,' said Ned.

'It's all I could find.'

'Hey, you know section nineteen?' said Paul.

'Yes,' said Ned hopefully.

'There was this most disgusting book. Victorian pornography, it was.'

'Wish I'd seen it,' said Ned.

'It was very explicit,' said Paul.

'I found your copy of Playboy in section twenty-three, Ned,' said Manfred.

'Yeah, well,' said Ned.

'You like the nude women do you, Ned?' said Manfred.

'Yeah, nothing wrong with that.'

'It's treating women as objects,' said Manfred.

'Well, they are, aren't they? Meant to be. Anyway, you mind your own business, Kraut.'

'Alright Ned.'

'That's better. Not only do you take our jobs but you tell us what to do.'

'I only tell you what I believe.'

'People shouldn't believe anything, it makes the world a worse place,' said Ned.

'Yeah, look at Ireland,' said Paul.

'My old woman used to believe in God. Sold on it she was. She used to get me to pray with her. I couldn't stand it. I used to go missing at bed times. And then the old rat-bag would hit me for not believing.' Ned laughed. 'But as I got older I used to hit her back, so then she'd leave me alone. I'll tell you what I do believe in, though. Beautiful women, good food and a fat pay cheque.'

'Ah, a hedonist,' said Manfred.

'Heda what?' said Ned.

'Someone who believes in enjoying themselves.'

'Hedonist is it? I must remember that and if anybody asks me what party I support I'll say: "I am a hedonist, sir".'

'You see, you do believe in something,' said Manfred.

'Yeah, but not much.'

'I know someone who believes in something,' said Manfred.

'Oh yeah,' said Ned.

'Yes, my friend Mark in York. He believes in the Holy Grail.'

'Holy Mackerel!'

'No, Holy Grail. He wants me to look up some references here.'

'What is this Holy Grail thing?'

'It is an ancient holy relic that has been lost for a long time.'

'Sounds a bit nutty to me.'

'I must admit I don't hold out much hope.'

'You going to look then?'

'Yes, of course.'

'Mind the librarian doesn't catch you. Likes of us aren't supposed to be reading old books.'

'I see no reason why not.'

'Books is for intellectual types.'

'Well, you say I'm intellectual, Ned.'

'Yeah, but you're a cleaner, Manfred. You've got to remember your place.'

'Bugger this "place".'

'I see you've been taught good English,' said Ned approvingly.

'According to Samuel Johnson, "bugger" is a term of affection amongst sailors,' said Manfred.

'Oh, that's a good one,' said Ned.

'Some of these old gentleman types knew a thing or two,' said Paul.

'Yeah, they don't make 'em like that nowadays,' said Ned.

'Well, excuse me, gentlemen. It is time I was working,' said Manfred, getting up from his seat.

'Yeah, I s'pose we better go,' said Paul.

The men put on their overalls and entered the round amphitheatre of the library. Dusters at the ready, they proceeded to their allotted sections, Manfred working speedily at his section throughout the morning, pausing now and then to dip into a book which interested him. Slowly he worked his way towards the manuscript room.

Just before lunchtime he was within a few yards of it. He looked around furtively, then went in. There was no-one there. He looked at the assembly of drawers, lost for a moment, then started to search amongst them. After fifteen minutes he came upon what he was looking for, a drawer entitled "Codex B Britannicus". He slid the drawer open and took out the vellum-bound book. It was handwritten in Latin but Manfred knew some Latin. He flicked through its pages.

Professor Thynne wrote a letter a to friend in Germany:

My dearest Wolfgang,

I am a trifle inspissated by the action of my electric fire but otherwise I am in good health. I have a question to ask you. As Simon de Limoges said, 'Let the question be asked.' My question is not however the question of the grand inquisitor. It is a question of mystery. 'God is dead,' as we all know but undoubtedly Jesus Christ existed. I believe this. And so too, undoubtedly did the Holy Grail, and it is this which I wish to ask you about. Tell me, Wolfgang, if you can, whether the Grail might be in Germany, lingering in some forgotten abbrevoir or else in one of those magnificent castles etcetera etcetera. We wish to discover it, and with it transform society and more personally I wish for something special to take with me into old age. We are making great efforts here in England. My friend, the artist Gerald Hagenbach, is planning to shoot a priest in order to uncover the secret. This is rash but I cannot reason with him.

Yours in hope,

Norwald Etwas Thynne. Ph.D. Oxon.

The day of the séance came. Dianna got everybody organised. They met round at Gerald's place. Norwald Thynne, Tristan, Chris, Mark, Alec and Robbie were there besides Gerald and Dianna. They were squeezed stomach to back in the kitchen.

'Listen everybody,' said Dianna, 'we're going to see Madame Elestrada and there's several things you've got to know. When she opens the door she'll say, "Who wishes admittance to the spirit world?" and one us has got to answer "In the name of God we do." And then she'll say, "And what fee do you bring me?" Then you've got to say, "We bring you silver". Then you offer her your hand and she leads you into the séance room. Alright?'

'Yes,' everybody mumbled.

'Shall we be going, then?'

'Can I bring Boris?' asked Gerald.

'No Gerald, you'd better not.'

'We'd better have a quick whip round,' said Chris.

'Yes, we'd better. We've got to raise twenty pounds,' said Dianna. The group fumbled in their pockets. Chris had two pence. Robbie had a ten pound note which he tried to get changed. Dianna had forgotten to bring any money and had nothing. Finally, however, they assembled twenty pounds and handed it to Dianna.

'We've got to put it in an envelope,' she said. 'It's bad etiquette to show the money.' This was done.

'Will the séance be conducted in Greek?' asked the poet.

'Don't be silly,' said Dianna.

'Oh. But all the best séances are conducted in Greek. All true oracles speak Greek.'

'Not this one.'

They set off. The party trundled through town, walking in twos. The professor led the procession. They had to wait for a few minutes as Alec went to a chemist's to buy some more cough mixture. Chris met a tramp he knew and this man joined the party, swilling cider as he walked. At last they were at the door of Madame Elestrada. It was a council house. The professor knocked ceremoniously and the door was opened.

'Spirits?' said Madame Elestrada with her arms crossed.

'That's right,' said Professor Thynne.

'Who wishes to be admitted to the spirit world?' said Madame Elestrada.

'Er… We do in the name of God,' declaimed the professor, holding his right hand over his heart.

'And what fee do you bring me?'

'We bring you silver. Blast, where is it?'

Dianna handed him the envelope which he passed on to the Madame. The professor then extended his right hand.

'It's your left one, twit!' said Madame.

'Oh. Oh yes, I see.'

The party went inside. They were led into a room where there was a round table with ten chairs around it, as if the party of nine had been expected. 'Pray be seated,' said Madame. She was dressed in a long black silk dress, which hugged her body and touched the floor. Over her shoulders she wore a feather boa. Her fingers were loaded with a dozen rings. She had green make-up on around her eyes and her lips were painted violet. The smell of the perfume she was wearing filled the room. She pulled the curtains across and took a seat with the party. In the silence she produced a small brass snuff box and took snuff. She offered it around the table. Gerald tried eating some. 'The proceedings commence,' said Madame. She rose from her chair, went into an empty space of the room and started spinning clockwise with her face turned upwards. Abruptly she stopped. 'Let the spirit world reign,' she said. She came back to the table and, out of an ornate box, retrieved some bones. These she put in front of her on the table as she sat down. She fumbled with the bones, arranging them in different patterns. 'Bones of Avernicus, yield to our will!' she declared. Suddenly her head fell forward on her chest and she started breathing deeply and rapidly. Her body shook and her hands shot above her head. Gerald began to giggle but Dianna quietened him. Suddenly she was still. She looked upward and with a blank face started talking in baby talk: 'Ooo's got mummy's scissors? Give me some sweeties. Mama Mama!' She started crying. A minute later the tears ceased and there was silence. The party waited breathlessly. Nothing happened. Gerald started to roll a cigarette but Dianna stopped him. There were several more minutes of silence. Finally, the professor stood to his feet and addressed Madam Elestrada.

'Er, spirit. Do you know Plotinus?' There was a pause.

'Sit down, you fool,' the spirit said hollowly.

'Oh! Oh dear,' mumbled the professor, sitting down rapidly.

'Who is it that has sought me?' asked the spirit. There was a pause.

'We do. Eight seekers of the Holy Grail,' said Dianna. There was a silence for several minutes.

'Ye seek the Grail,' said the spirit. There was more silence.

'We do,' affirmed Dianna.

'Seek the Grail in Aachen…Seek the Grail in Bonn…Seek the Grail in Thailand…Seek the Grail in the Don…Seekers, ye are lost,' said the spirit.

'What's it on about?' said Chris to Robbie.

'Is it in Germany?' asked Professor Thynne.

'The Grail flees onward outpacing its pursuers. Distant it is. Yes, surely it is distant,' said the spirit.

'Yes but is it in Germany?' asked the professor impatiently.

'I have spoken to you before, old man, you are not my chosen one,' said the spirit.

'Am I your chosen one?' asked Dianna.

'You are not.'

'Me?' asked Chris.

'No.'

'Me?' asked Robbie.

'No.'

'Me?' asked Mark.

'No.'

'Well, how about me?' said Alec.

'No.'

'Me?' asked the tramp.

'No.'

'Me?' said Tristan, raising his hand.

'No.' Everybody turned towards Gerald, who was scratching himself.

'Is it Gerald?' asked Dianna. The spirit was silent. 'Gerald, ask the spirit if it's you,' said Dianna.

'Is it me?' asked Gerald in a muffled voice.

'Gerald Hagenbach, it is you.' Everyone gasped.

'How did you know my name?' demanded Gerald. The spirit was silent. 'Who told it my name?'

'Gerald, ask it about the Grail,' said Dianna urgently.

'I don't like people knowing my name,' said Gerald.

'Gerald, shut up and ask the question,' whispered Dianna.

'Where is the Holy Grail?' asked Gerald.

'Over the sea and far away,' said the spirit.

'I told you it was in Germany,' said the professor.

'Silence, Thynne. You are forbidden to speak,' said the spirit.

'Oh my goodness! Pardon me,' said the professor.

'Whereabouts?' asked Gerald.

'Empty the room – except Gerald,' said the spirit.

Eight people got up and obediently left the room. Outside Dianna put her ear to the keyhole. She could hear nothing. Ten minutes later Gerald came to the door. 'You can come back in now,' he said. The party trooped back inside and sat down. Madam Elestrada was moaning faintly.

'Gerald, what did it say?' whispered Dianna.

'I don't know,' said Gerald.

'Gerald?'

'This whole thing is a farce,' boomed the professor.

'You go too far, Thynne,' said the spirit.

'Don't spoil it, Norwald,' said Chris.

'Thynne, you will come to a bad end,' said the spirit. 'You will become covered in warts and look hideous like a toad.'

'Oh, how could you?' remonstrated the professor.

'It is fate,' said the spirit.

'Spirit, could you tell Gerald again about the Holy Grail. He says he doesn't know,' said Dianna.

'Gerald knows, but I have sworn him to secrecy.'

'Rotter,' said Robbie.

'Terrible harm shall befall him he if reveals the secret.'

'It's up to you, Gerald,' said Chris.

'What about me?' asked the tramp. Madame's body jerked violently.

'Awie man, Jimmy,' said the (presumably new) spirit.

'Is that Rex?' said the tramp.

'Och aye,' said the spirit of Rex.

'How are you getting on?'

'Well there isnae nae booze up here but it's alright for a laugh.'

'Do you remember that time we got chucked out of the theatre for having a fight?'

'Aye, ah do, Jimmy.'

'What'll happen to me, Rex?'

'Why, you'll end up like me.'

'In heaven?'

'Limbo, laddie, limbo.'

'How do I get to heaven?' There was no answer. 'Rex?'

There was no answer. The tramp started crying. Dianna comforted him. Professor Thynne stood up. 'I demand the spirit of Nietzsche,' he said. Again Madame's body jerked.

'Why, hello!' said a voice in an American accent.

'Is that Nietzsche?' the professor said doubtfully.

'It sure ain't.'

'But I want Nietzsche.'

'Well you got me.'

'Who are you?'

'Allesandro Ravetti.'

'And what did you do?'

'I was a comedian.'

'What are you now?'

'A bad comedian.'

'Oh.'

'You want some advice?'

'Well, I'll try some.'

'Lay off Wagner. He's a bore.'

'Never.'

'All those long moaning meandering lines sung by jerks with horns on their heads.'

'This is preposterous.'

The spirit laughed mockingly.

'You Americans have no culture.'

'Go hang yourself, Thynne.'

'Really!' Madame Elestrada moaned. 'You're going? Come back, I order you! I haven't finished with you yet.'

Madame stopped moaning and sat upright. 'The doors to the spirit world are closed,' she said.

'Oh, just when it was getting good,' said Robbie.

'You will leave now,' said Madame.

The company rose and left the house. The professor muttered to himself and Tristan consoled him. Gerald walked in front, his head hung down. The eyes of the others were on him. 'Lucky sod,' said Chris.

'Well, he always was special,' said Dianna.

Mark was telephoning Graals again.

'Hello, Simon Graal here.'

'I'm interested in your name.'

'I'm interested too.'

'Graal is the old word for Grail, and I'm interested in whether you have any old stories about it in the family.'

'About the Holy Grail?'

'That's right.'

'How much will you give me for it?'

'I was hoping you'd volunteer the information.'

'No.'

'Could you tell me whether you know anything important?'

'Yes, it's very important.'

'Well…'

'I was going to make up a story about it and charge you. No, I don't know anything about it.'

'Oh.' Mark tried another number.

'Grail, there never was a Grail,' Marion Graal said.

'Well, do you know if there are any stories about your name?'

'Well, it's old French for "dish". The family is probably descended from metal workers.'

This was disappointing, a blow to the effort. Far from being descendants of the Knights of King Arthur, the Graals could merely have been artisans. He had another setback.

'Graal. Yes, It's old Icelandic for a blow on the head. One of our ancestors probably got into a fight.'

Again.

'Grail. No, never heard of it.'

And again.

'Don't waste my time.'

But –

'Grail. Yes, we have a story about it. The story goes that one of our ancestors obtained a fragment of it. We've still got it today, actually.'

'Really?'

'Yes, it's gold, so we keep it in a bank vault. For the gold alone it must be worth a lot.'

'Can I see it some day?' They made arrangements. 'Are there any stories about what happened to the rest of it?' asked Mark.

'Well, the fragments are supposed to have been distributed amongst the Knights of various countries and taken abroad.'

Mark was inspired to continue the enquiries. He drew several more blanks. But then:

'You're interested in my name, are you? I bet I know why. You've heard that we won the pools.'

'No.'

'What then?'

'Well, I'm interested in the Holy Grail, and Graal is the old way of spelling it.'

'The Grail. Oh, that old thing. We had a professor enquiring for the same reason.'

'It wasn't a Professor Thynne, was it?'

'No, it was a Professor Barrel.'

'And do you know anything?'

'Yes, as a matter of fact. Our family came from Brittany originally and our founding member is supposed to have been granted his name for having rescued the Grail from the lake.'

'Do you know which lake?'

'No, except that it was in Brittany.'

'You don't know what happened to it after that?'

'The church is supposed to have taken possession of it.'

'You don't know what date that was?'

'I'm afraid not.'

The next call was to Birmingham. 'Yes,' a querulous voice answered.

'I'm interested in the Holy Grail.'

'Well, you can't have it.'

'You've mean you've got it?'

'A little piece of it. I keep it under my mattress.'

'Your mattress?'

'Oh, I shouldn't have told you that, you might be a thief.'

'Could I come and see it?'

'No. I don't trust you. I've said enough already.'

'Please, I'm genuinely interested.'

The phone cut off. Mark tried another Birmingham number.

'Grail! You're a joker.'

'No, I'm serious.'

'You want your head examined.'

'Possibly.'

Andrew had left Iona and had broken his journey at Mark's on the way south.

'And I'll swear that ninety percent of them were unreformed criminals,' Andrew said.

Mark laughed. 'Well, if you ever think of retiring, Andrew, there's the place for you to go,' he said.

'Most certainly not.'

'And did you find out anything about the Grail?'

'Well, according to the Abbot Sylvester, it may be in France or it may have been buried on the island.'

'We could go up there with metal detectors.'

'A whole island to cover, though. How about you, Mark, did you find anything?'

'It may be in Singapore. It may be in France. It may be in Lancaster, and two people say they've got fragments of it, one of them in York. I'm going to see it soon.'

'So we've got a fair range of places to choose from. But we've got two people saying it may be in France. That outweighs the other bits of information.'

'France, yes. Still, we'll have to wait and see before we do anything drastic.'

'You're prepared to go abroad, then?'

'Yes, I'm convinced enough.'

'Have we got anything else?'

'Well, my friend Manfred at the British Museum found a reference which suggests that it's in Germany.'

'Germany now.'

'And there's Gerald, of course.'

'What about Gerald?'

'A medium told him where it was at a séance, but he's been sworn to secrecy under threat.'

'Oh Gawd.'

'He's our main hope so far.'

'What about the professor?'

'He's still waiting to hear from his friend in Germany. The spirit was quite rude to him. It was funny, it told him that Wagner was a bore and he should give it up.'

'Well, that's one spirit I approve of.'

'I went round to see Gerald the other day.'

'Was he well?'

'I don't know. He was out but it was really funny. You know he says he keeps getting electric shocks off things, even when they're turned off? He's dead scared of electricity. Well, I happened to notice his electricity meter while I was there. It had stopped at six six six.'

'The number of the great beast of the apocalypse.'

'Yes, and with Gerald not there it was as if he'd seen it and freaked right out.'

'Poor Gerald.'

'I suppose so, but he does some funny things.'

'Yes, though he's tougher than we all think. You know Michael once said to me, "Gerald is a survivor – no matter what he gets into, he'll find a way through it". The odd laugh at his expense won't hurt him. That reminds me, can I make a quick telephone call to Maria and see if he's alright?' Andrew went to the phone. 'Hello Maria. God bless you.'

'Oh Andrew, how are you?'

'Well a bit the worse for wear, but enjoying life on the whole.'

'That's good.'

'Tell me Maria, have you seen Gerald recently, or heard anything of him?'

'No, I haven't seen him, but he scampers around all night above me, playing the one-note symphony.'

Andrew laughed. 'So he's probably alright ,then?' he asked.

'I should think so.'

'Well, thanks very much. Goodbye and God bless.' He put the phone down. 'Did you hear?' he said to Mark.

'No.'

'He's been playing his music all night. Poor Maria, she's right below him, it must disturb her.'

'Yes, I remember how it was when Gerald stayed with me. Except that it was mostly Mozart.'

'Gosh, yes, I remember, the same piano concerto over and over again. I almost knew that music by heart.'

'Gerald used to compare himself with Mozart.'

'You mean he identified with him?'

'That's right.'

'Well, at least he's not into Wagner, that would be too much to bear.'

'He's got an old record of the Laughing Policeman now.'

Andrew laughed.

'You're just staying overnight?' said Mark.

'Yes, overnight and then I must push on down South.'

'I got some extra vegetables in.'

'Oh, thank you. So I don't need to buy anything? Good.'

'What are you reading now?'

'Well, you'll laugh. It's Piggy Woodruff Goes To Town.'

Mark laughed. 'You'll be on Enid Blyton next.'

'Never, can't stand her.'

'Piggy Woodruff and the Bible. Which do you find more profound?'

'Now, Mark.'

'What does Piggy Woodruff do?'

'Eats a lot and dresses in striped pyjamas.'

'Is it a Christian piggy?'

'Undoubtedly.'

'Well, that's alright then.'

'You're still not a Christian, Mark?'

'No, not me.'

'Well, don't give up on the Grail.'

'Not yet, anyway.'

'Do you mind if I turn on the radio?' Andrew turned it on. Some organ music was playing. 'Ah, Bach, Bach, my favourite.'

'Bach! I'll introduce you to Sam and The Psychos.'

'They sound revolting.'

'Good to dance to.'

'They sound as if they're good to knife people to.'

Mark laughed. 'Yes Andrew, you should grow your hair long, as Gerald says you should, and wear a pink flowery shirt.'

'And black fishnet stockings.'

'Did Gerald say that too?'

'Yes. And over them I've got to wear shorts.'

'Well, there's time yet.'

'That'd shock my religious friends. I'd walk in and say "Hi man" with two fingers up in the peace sign.'

'Go on, Andrew, give it a try.'

There was a party out in the country at Gemima's, a friend of Alec's. Loud music played and there were people lying on the floor. In one corner were Alec, Gerald, Dianna, and a friend of Alec's called Nick. Gerald was discoursing to Dianna about love.

'Yes Gerald,' said Dianna.

'And it should be simple. Love should be simple. None of this "What are you doing wearing my bra?" or anything like that.'

'Are you wearing a bra, Gerald?'

'Yes. And if you love someone you should go to bed with them. It's no good just kissing.'

'Kissing's nice, Gerald.'

'Not unless it's in bed.'

'I don't know.'

'True love should be like Dante and Beatrice. They probably went to bed together.'

'Yes Gerald.'

'You should be able to go up and say to someone, "I love you, will you come to bed with me?" But everyone's so inhibited that it doesn't happen.'

'Love has to be proved, Gerald.'

'Nonsense. I mean, I love you, but it's no good because Robbie's in the way.'

'Yes, Gerald.'

'People always try to get in the way and stop you doing what you want. Andrew's like that. He's always trying to stop me doing what I want.'

'True love is of God,' murmured Alec.

'Yes, but God doesn't go to bed with you,' said Gerald.

'My one does,' Dianna laughed.

'People try to get in the way of love. They say "My life's miserable, why should yours be any better?"' said Gerald.

'People are a nuisance.'

'Yes. I like your skirt, Dianna, it's really good.'

'Thank you, Gerald.'

'But people shouldn't wear clothes.'

'It'd be a bit cold, Gerald.'

'People shouldn't wear clothes because God made us naked. People just wear clothes because they're inhibited.'

'That's not the only reason.'

'It is. You can't love someone if they're wearing clothes.'

'You think love is the same as sex.'

'Yes, that's right, they're the same. If only people wouldn't play games with each other and lie.'

'I don't agree with that, Gerald.'

'It's true. People are always playing games and lying. I mean, I play games and lie sometimes.'

Robbie came into the room at that point and interrupted the conversations. 'Hi folks. Hey, I'm going to write a book called Baba And Hipster Rhythm.'

'What?' exclaimed Dianna delightedly.

'Yeah,' said Robbie, pleased with the impression he'd made.

'What's it going to be about, Robbie?'

'Oh you know, Kerouac, Ginsberg, the jazz scene, drugs.'

'Go on, Robbie.'

'I don't know whether I'll get round to it or not. Writing's such a drag.'

'I wrote a story last week,' said Dianna.

'What about?'

'It was about this prince and princess and they kept passing through mirrors to other worlds.'

'Sounds far out.'

'Yes, it was, but it only lasted two pages.'

'How's your painting, Dianna?'

'Oh, alright. I did this painting of a prophet.'

Gerald, who'd been moping at having lost the attention of Dianna, butted in. 'I am a prophet.'

Dianna and Robbie laughed. 'What do you prophesy?' asked Dianna.

'I prophesy that the Blacks and the Jews will rise up against the oppression of society and create a new world.'

'Fair enough,' said Robbie.

'And that all those who practise racial hatred will be struck dead by God.'

'There you go again.'

'Yes, and the motor car will be destroyed and twisted up.'

'Oh?'

'Yes. People worship the motor car. The motor car is not God. The motor car is the Devil.'

'That's a bit extreme.'

'No, it's not. A goddamn pile of metal on wheels. Why do you love it? You can't love a pile of metal. All it does is kill people and stink. I was nearly run over by a car the other day. They have no feelings. No beauty…Then we'll have nature and everyone will be upper class.'

'Why upper class? What's wrong with being middle class?'

'Middle class is better than working class but it's not good enough. My parents came from Holland. They should be treated like aristocrats. I'm aristocratic.'

At that point Mark entered the room with a drink in his hand. As he sat down he spoke. 'I was nearly possessed by the Devil last Wednesday.' Everyone laughed.

'How did it happen, Mark?' asked Dianna.

'Well, I was lying in bed feeling a bit bored with the astral body I was wearing and I started trying others. I tried all the people I knew without any luck and then I tried more way out ones. I asked for Tutankhamun, Nebuchanezzar and the Devil. I didn't mean it seriously. But then there was this shimmering and shaking all over and I could feel something new entering my aura. So I said a quick prayer to God and it went away. The trouble was I couldn't stop saying "the Devil" in my thoughts and he kept coming back at me so I had to keep praying. It makes me tempted to believe in God.'

'You should, you know, Mark,' said Robbie.

'But it could just be the person who put me in this state playing a hoax and trying to frighten me.'

'It's the Devil, Mark' said Dianna.

'I didn't sleep at all that night, and I had to put the light on.'

'Yeah, it's funny how having a light on makes things seem less evil,' said Robbie.

'Anyway, that's my news. Have you got any? How about the Holy Grail?' Nick came over. 'We're trying to find the Holy Grail,' said Mark. Nick started laughing.

'Alright. Alright. You can help us, anyway.'

'Leave me out of this,' said Nick.

'Look, you're a goldsmith. How would you know if something you had was made of gold?'

Nick pulled his beard. 'You want Aqua Regia.'

'Aqua Regia?'

'Yes, it's a mixture of nitric and sulphuric acids. Gold is the only metal which doesn't dissolve in it.'

'That's worth knowing. Thanks.'

The party continued. By this time many people were lying on the floor locked in embraces. The music churned on. 'How are you, Nick?' asked Robbie, munching a stuffed vine leaf.

'Business as usual.'

'Have you set up a jewellery workshop yet?'

'No, there's nowhere to put it.'

'You should have stayed in Corsica.'

'No, I'm glad I got out. I was starving in Corsica. It was alright during the tourist season, but in winter everybody's got to borrow and starve. I spent seven years sweating my guts out there, and what for? Nothing, absolutely nothing. I'm better off here, except it's so boring.'

'Why don't you join in with us, then, and look for the Holy Grail?'

'No thank you.'

'Why not?'

'I'm too busy trying to keep my head together. I don't want to loosen a hinge joining in with your crazy schemes.'

'That's a pity.'

'Anyway, you'll never find it. Why not go looking for Eldorado instead?'

'Yeah, I fancy that too.'

'Or Atlantis.'

'I'll do that after we've found the Grail.'

Meanwhile, Gerald, having seen Mark talking to a woman on the other side of the room, thought he'd try the same thing. He looked around until he found a solitary woman. 'Can I sit next to you?' he said.

The woman made no answer so Gerald sat down.

'I'm an artist,' he said.

'I'm a chemist's assistant.'

'Norwald Thynne is an artist too, but he's in league with the forces of darkness.'

The woman edged away from him.

'What do you think about true love?' said Gerald. The woman was silent and looked straight ahead. 'I mean, you're beautiful. I really love you.' The woman turned red. 'You're like a painting off a Greek vase.' The woman started fidgeting. 'I like everything to be feminine. Masculine equals aggression. That's why I wear tights.' The woman continued fidgeting. 'Do you want to see my tights? I'll show them to you if you want,' said Gerald eagerly. The woman blew her nose. 'Why don't you talk to me?' Pause. 'You won't talk to me because I've got an affliction.' The woman got up and left the room. Gerald came over to where the others were sitting. 'She won't talk to me because I've got an affliction,' he said.

'What's that, Gerald, have you freaked someone else out?' asked Dianna.

'What's wrong with me? It's other people who are wrong. You tell someone they're beautiful and they spit at you.'

'Did she spit at you?'

'No, but you know what I mean.'

'You'll never learn, Gerald.'

'What is there to learn? Love should be simple. I can't stand people that make it complicated. Do you want a dance, Dianna?'

'Alright, Gerald.'

Gerald went to the middle of the room and started dancing, a dance which consisted of running on the spot. Dianna joined him.

Andrew was in Walsingham. He'd arrived there after much difficulty on the road and after having nearly been run over. However, he had arrived.

He was speaking to Nancy, a nun. 'Nancy, I don't suppose you know anything about the Holy Grail, do you?'

'Shhh,' Nancy said, putting a finger to her lips.

'What?'

'Don't speak so loudly. Come with me.'

The nun led him to the rear of the building through a winding passage, then opened a creaking oak door. 'This way,' she said. They first descended to one layer of cellars, and then through a trap-door to a second. Nancy lit a candle.

'Oh, I say, this is rather mysterious,' said Andrew.

'You'll understand soon. Only, be quiet.'

'Sorry.'

The nun took Andrew through several rooms of the cellar and stopped in the third one. 'Wait,' she said. The room was cluttered with old boxes. She went to one side of the room and started pulling boxes away. Suddenly, Andrew saw something gleam. Nancy pulled out the object triumphantly. 'One of my friends found it when he was digging in the garden,' she said.

Andrew looked on. It looked to be a golden chalice of the shape he'd imagined the Grail to be. 'My word!' he exclaimed.

'Shhh!'

'Sorry. Can I have a look at it, Nancy?' Andrew whispered. Nancy handed it to Andrew. 'Is it gold?' he asked.

'Yes, I think so – feel the weight of it.'

'Gosh, yes.' He peered at the chalice excitedly, drawing closer to Nancy for a share of the candlelight. 'It's got a hallmark on it.'

'Oh.'

'No, it can't be the Grail. But why are you hiding it?'

'We want to sell it. A nun's life is hard.'

'Are you sure that's proper, Nancy?'

'No, it's not proper, but one of the nuns, the one who found it, wants to retire from the settlement.'

'Oh, well. I won't tell anyone. Mother Church is stinking rich as it is.' Nancy started giggling. 'What is it, Nancy?'

'I shouldn't be down here with a man, especially not at night.'

'You're in safe hands.'

Nancy gave him a funny look. 'Shall we go up, Andrew?' She packed the chalice away and led Andrew upstairs. 'You're sure you won't tell anyone?' she whispered, when they reached the top.

'Scout's honour.'

'Were you a scout, Andrew?'

'No.'

'Well, think of something else then.'

'The Bible forbids the swearing of oaths.'

'But you won't tell?'

'No.'

'That's alright then. I shouldn't have shown it to you really. Goodnight, Andrew.'

Andrew left the building to go to the outhouse where he was staying. On the way a stray dog tried to pick a fight with Jock but was shooed away by Andrew. Andrew felt disappointment, but despite the failure of the chalice to be the Holy Grail, he was cheered up by having seen it, and had the irrational feeling that progress was being made. He went to bed. The next morning he visited the shrine of Our Lady, mingling with a crowd of pilgrims.

'Hello, Andrew,' a voice said. Andrew spun round.

'Who? Oh, it's Geoffrey, hello,' he said, pleased.

'Well, it's a long time since I've seen you,' said Geoffrey.

'Oh, I've been here there and everywhere.'

'Do you remember when we last met at Prinknash?'

'Yes, yes I do, Geoffrey. That was a long time ago. We've both been on the road longer than we should have been.'

'Gentlemen of the road, that's us. Do they still mistake you for a priest, Andy?'

'Yes, it still happens.'

'Is that your dog?'

'Yes, I wouldn't be parted from him now. He's terribly good company.'

'I once had a cat myself. Used to travel everywhere with me.'

'Did you lose it?'

'Yes, it ran off somewhere in Glastonbury. Don't blame it, poor little thing. What are you doing these days, Andy?'

'Oh, travelling around. And I'm looking for the Holy Grail.'

'Holy Grail, is it? Isn't it supposed to be in Germany?'

'Haven't a clue. We keep getting indications that it's all over the place. A retired professor I know thinks it's in Germany, though.'

'Yes, Germany. This wandering scholar I met had a talk to me about it and he swore it was in Germany.'

'Well, the more clues the better.'

'Will you go to Germany?'

'What? With Jock? No, I can't, we wouldn't get past the quarantine regulations. Besides I'd never have the money. I'd love to travel, though. I dearly would.'

'I could lend you the money.'

'You? Money?'

'An old aunt left me a bit.'

'A tramp with a bank account.'

'Yes, it softens life a bit.'

'But no home?'

'No, Andrew.'

'Well, the good Lord will provide.'

'He'd better provide soon before I'm too old for this game.'

'How old are you now, Geoffrey?'

'Sixty-two.'

'Yes, it's time we were both settling down. But do you think you could get used to a settled life, Geoffrey?'

'I'll say I could. I'm fed up of this existence.'

'The Lord gives us strength.'

'The Lord gives us a hard time.'

Andrew laughed. 'Well, as Teresa of Avila said, "Lord, is this how you treat your friends? No wonder you haven't many".'

'I'm beginning to think like that, Andy.'

'I don't blame you. But things are bound to get better.'

'You're an optimist.'

'Yes, I'm an optimist. You have to be in this life. If it wasn't for optimism, I would have given up and died years ago.'

'I suppose you're right, Andy. Put a brave face on and all that. Well, you seem so healthy and cheery, you inspire me to keep going.'

'Do I? That's nice.'

'Well, I'd better just say a little prayer and then I'll be going. See you, Andy.'

'May God be with you, Geoffrey.'

Later that day Andrew was taken to see the Mother Superior. In a wooden panelled, well-lit room, he sat at a desk embarrassedly waiting for Mother Superior to stop picking her nose. Finally she leant back in her chair and waved a hand negligently.

'Andrew, you're a nice boy.'

'Oh, thank you,' said Andrew doubtfully.

'You remind me of my brother. He had a face just like yours. He went into the army.'

'Oh, yes?'

'He played the trombone in a military band.' There was a pause. 'Do you play the trombone?'

'No, Mother Superior.'

'Were you in the army?'

'Well, I was for a spell but I hated it. I couldn't take it seriously, but I managed to dodge the square bashing, and got myself a job helping the curate.'

'Where were you?'

'In Japan.'

'My brother was stationed in Borneo. So you can't be my brother. Pity.'

'The resemblance fades.'

'Anyway, I used to hate my brother.'

'Oh.'

'Yes, he used to hit me.'

'Indeed?'

'You'll just have to be my brother in Christ. How is your situation now, Andrew? Is it any better that when I last saw you?'

'No, still the same. But I've found something to do. I'm looking for the Holy Grail.'

'Really – well I believe I can help you,' said Mother Superior attentively.

'You can?'

'Yes, we have an ancient manuscript that details various holy relics. According to our manuscript, the Grail was taken to Magdeburg in Germany.'

'Germany again!'

'Why, has someone else said the same?'

'Yes, just recently.'

'Well, you must go to Germany, then.'

'No, it's impossible for me for many reasons, and anyway I can't speak German. I'll pass the news on to my friends in York.'

'Do others search for it?'

'Yes, several.'

'Well, God bless you in your search then. You must go now, I have work to do.'

'Thank you, Mother Superior.'

Andrew left the building and crossed a cloister. Jock spotted a bitch and jerked the lead out of his hand. He ran after him and grabbed the lead. 'Really, Jock! Not here of all places,' he said. He continued back to the building where he had been boarded and sat on the bed in his room. Travelling as he did, he got to know so many different people. There was Geoffrey, the Mother Superior, and he knew many of the other nuns by name. It was the same wherever he went. He had the knack of friendliness and of making friends.

Professor Thynne was in his room with Tristan. A pile of 'Grails' lay in the middle of the bed. Professor Thynne looked out of the window with his hands behind his back. 'I am a second Nietzsche,' he said.

'Yes, Norwald.'

'I philosophise with a hammer, as did Nietzsche.'

'Yes, Norwald.'

'I might even be the Superman,' he said, drawing in his stomach. 'Der Übermensch,' he added.

'I'm sure you are,' said Tristan.

'Oh, you think so? How kind.'

'Well, you know more than most people.'

'Yes, I do.'

'You don't think I've found the Grail then, do you Norwald?'

'No, Tristan, I'm afraid not; we must make further efforts.'

'Have you got anything in mind, Norwald?'

'It's in Germany, without a doubt. I kept telling everyone but no-one would listen.'

'You're always right, Norwald.'

'Thank you, Tristan. I've had a letter from Wolfgang Somerkind, which proves beyond a doubt that the Grail either is or has been in Germany. I'll read it to you in a minute.'

'Can I dust your books, Norwald?'

'Of course.'

'Look what clever me found,' said Tristan, holding up a feather duster.

'My goodness, what's that, Tristan?'

'It's a feather duster like housewives use.'

'Oh, I see. Very good.'

Tristan rose to his feet and crossed to the bookshelves. Humming gently, he flicked the duster at the books. The professor turned round and watched him. 'There's no place like home, as they say,' he said, smiling. Tristan continued humming. 'I wonder what that bungler Freud would have thought of this?' Professor Thynne remarked. 'A longing to please mother, Oedipal complex probably. Have you an Oedipal complex, Tristan?'

'If you say so, Norwald.'

'Do you see me as your mother, Tristan?'

'Sometimes, Norwald.'

'It's even better than the virgin birth, what? Mind you, dust Wagner thoroughly. We can't have Wagner defiled by dust. Anyway, let me read you this letter.' He picked up the letter from the floor and waved the crumbs off it.

My dear Norwald,

I was very interested to hear of your desire to find the Holy Grail and I have therefore made strenuous efforts. I have consulted many sources but principally Frühchristliche Studien, Akten der Münchener Jagd- Schiess- und Graalsuchgesellschaft, Jahresberichte des Nellingsheimer Heimatsmuseums and Akten der Teutonischen Ritter. These all contained a wealth of information about the Grail. It is heartening that they are all unanimous in saying that the Grail came to Germany. Firstly it is said to have arrived in Magdeburg and then to have been taken to Dinkelsbühl in Southern Germany. The reports say that at that time it had not lost any of its radiance and is reputed to have blinded several people, presumably sinners. So far, I have been unable to trace what happened to it after Dinkelsbühl, but I will keep searching and write to you again. I am surprised that you are interested, with your sympathy for Nietzsche and therefore atheism, but you always were a man of many contrasts. I hope your friend Tristan is in good health. Sorry about your electric fire.

Heartily yours,

Wolfgang.

'There, you see?' said Professor Thynne, waving the letter triumphantly. 'And you notice he asks after you, Tristan?'

'It's very nice of him, Norwald.'

'Magdeburg, Dinkelsbühl – the obvious places for it. It would make sense if it went on to Tübingen, but we shall see.'

'Shall we go to Germany, Norwald?'

'Yes certainly, but we must wait and see what else Wolfgang turns up.'

'Oh, I would like to go, Norwald. All those clever philosophers and men in leather shorts.'

'And wine festivals and Wagner. We shall stay with Winifred.'

'Are you sure, Norwald? I'm not very good at mixing with society.'

'Nonsense, Tristan, you'd enjoy it. You'd be taken out hunting wild boar. What do you think of that?'

'I can't ride, Norwald.'

'It's easy, Tristan, you just sit there with a spear or whatever they are and the horse trots along without any trouble. You'll have to learn hunting songs, though. Meanwhile, we must let everyone else know about this letter.'

Word spread of the professor's letter, and there was a general consensus of desire to go to Germany. Arrangements were made for fund-raising efforts. Gerald and the professor decided to have art exhibitions. Chris Stricken started selling poems on street corners. Robbie started dealing in cocaine. Alec went to his parents for money. Mark started advertising his marbled papers more, and Dianna said she'd manage somehow. So far Professor Thynne had not become covered with warts, although there was plenty of time for that to happen. Gerald, though, what of Gerald? Callers to his flat often found him absent and it was rumoured that he went on forays for the Grail; certainly no-one could get him to say where he went. Andrew came and went on his ceaseless round of travel, out of the quest now but keeping a benevolent eye on the progress. There were two new seekers of the Grail: Tony the tramp, who centred his fund-raising activities around a spree of shoplifting, and the priest whom Gerald had met. The priest, whose name was Alfred, had visited Gerald's flat and afterwards been introduced to the professor. Intent on adding glory to his church, he added respectability to the quest.

It was approaching Christmas now and the weather was severe. Andrew holed up at a friend's house in the south of England. Gerald took to his bed for most of the day and Robbie took to his couch. Mark worked on in his workshop, the carragheen moss size sometimes freezing overnight. He installed a heater. A journalist from the local paper got to hear of the hunt for the Grail and attempted to interview Gerald about it, but came away confused, without a story, except for allegations of black magic and pleas for him to find Gerald a girlfriend. The Archbishop of York, Doctor Goodman, heard of the quest from the priest and wrote to the professor summoning him to an interview, but he was left with his head spinning; tales of Wagner, Nietzsche, Schopenhauer and Hegel left him not a whit the wiser.

The resolve of the Grail seekers was strengthened by the professor's news and even Alec became enthusiastic. It was a definite lead. Undaunted by the prospect of travel overseas, now they would look in earnest…

(January 1985)

Poems

Mark started writing poetry very early in life. His first poem, written when was eight years old, is included here. The poems in the 'London' section date back to his late teens; the darker themes of the 'York and 'Self' sections are mainly from the early Eighties, and the three marbling poems are recent work. This section of the anthology opens with four recent poems which celebrate his love of walking in the Scottish mountains.

SCOTLAND

Two ravens overhead
Their jagged voices
Echoing amongst the boulders
Broke the uneasy silence
With their wildness.

I am one
Of nature's secret kings
For alone
Amongst the mountains
A man can have dignity.

On a moor
I rested and listened
And a skylark
Answered my question
With a song.

In the shadow
Of the great mountain
I slept me
At one
With the natural world.

LONDON

Stars flashing under lamplight
In tossed hair and bouncing limbs
The scent of patchouli
Traintime down the street
Play on, you cosmic heroes.

ॐ

When I was a little boy
I could sing high E or E flat
Clear as a bell
You should've seen me!
Funny pink-faced cherub
With a ruff and a white surplice
Playing noughts and crosses
Under the pews
And praying that Shirley
Would fall in love with me.
Then sneaking in
In the dark
Pulling out all the stops
And making a terrific din
In the empty building.
Oh you funny little creature
Was I really you?

ॐ

She was gathering clover leaves
In the garden
Amongst the dew
And her hair
Was hanging loose to her waist
Capturing the sunlight
In the gentle breeze
In which the flowers unfolded
Trees whispered
And birds began to sing to her
And when she knew
That it was time
She stood up
And vanished
With the dewdrops.

ॐ

The Snake Charmer

The moon, shadows,
Cool dark shades,
Green glowing, gently
Moving

A soft breeze
A flute, plays
Stirring the air

Ripples
Like sand, hair

Dark, soft,
The music purrs

The sounds fall
Colours
Of the sunset

Of the flowers
Blood red, citrine
Eye blue,

The grasses stand
Ankle high, waist high
Waving

The lake, pale green,
Crystal fish
Emerge, spit at flies

A flamingo nearby
Not looking

A tiger crawls
Unseen
Somewhere the tiger
Sleeps
Amongst orchids,

The grasses part
Let through
A cinnamon worm

A tongue flickers
Another, glides down
From a branch

Body grows
Another branch,
Listens

The player sways,
Softly, by the lake

A rainbow serpent
Slides ashore

ॐ

Now is your time
Butterflies gather round the buddleia
Thistledown drifts in the breeze
Now is your time
I see you
Gentle, radiant, hopeful,
Full of some mystery
Some new life
Gently you gather your energies
A gift of a courgette
And a smile on
Your way out
Of this sleepy town
Will life be kind?

The woman has come

Star-freckled and ginger eyed smiling
She wears clothes
A ragamuffin would've been proud of
And her hair, goldilocks rattails.
O woman that's a jaunty smile
You have there, can I borrow it?
I'll be with you whole poet
But you'll have to write about me,
O I'll write flute notes in your hair
And your face by candlelight
You'll kindle me,
You and your fires,
Here's a quiet hand now
Take it, let's be gentle together
And so we love.

Maiden dancing in the meadow
The flowers dance in garlands
A young man will answer
Maiden, will your children dance too?
Yes! she cries, laughs and dances away.

ॐ

YORK

The city is alive with worship
In its haze of heat and light
The orthodox dart
Threadbare in sequins
Electric through its murmurs
The shadows are gorged with footsteps
And the pavements with shadows
The streets echo with song,
The faithful progress laughing
Through the heavy hectic facades
They conspire amongst and for

Around them and above
Hands uncup
Release sentences into the tepid air

The shadows of voices
Walk the streets in silence

Passing through the boundaries of words
Passing, just passing

It is accepted.

ॐ

Fulford Cemetery

There is something liquid in this warmth
We drift absorbed in,
That erodes the hard edges of thoughts
That erodes hard angles
Softened by birdsong and blossom.

The sounds of our voices drift between us
Dropped into the sunshine to bask
And pass away.

Beyond the trees people work
Silently, eyes to the ground
To clear away the wildness.

The jet carapace of a beetle disappears
Amongst the grass stalks
A laburnum grows by the path.

ॐ

A bird sings in my mouth
Sings me into the suns
Which weigh down my eyes
Speaks me to tomorrow's eclipse
What a lie, this sunshine
It sings the intensity of a carved inscription
In the confusion of centuries,
Its harshness, its mockery – its stillness
Its refusal and its independence,
I do not know the inscription.

But it is like the hastily tied knot
Which secured the sails in a storm
Or the smugglers' boat,
The hand which was risked
Reassuring through prison bars,
A word which made a difference.

A song sung for the hell of it
For the heaven of it
For a laugh
Recklessly tender
Sung with the authority of dream

ॐ

My Sister: The House Has No Walls

She packs up her troubles
She packs up the troubles of the world
In a wooden box,
Playtime is over.
Deftly she catches one last small trouble,
It is the lie that she let them out
In the first place.
She watches them seethe
She is a connoisseur of troubles.

She explains that the box is not her womb
Although her womb has been used
For this purpose,
And that her womb
Is not a hungry carnivore
Enchanted by incense
Or subdued by poisonous fumes.

She says that she is not to be conjured against
In this way
That it is not necessary
To make such a fuss
She says it is interesting
Look! I will show you
I am not ashamed.

She climbs on the jagged railings
And takes an apple
It is merely a beautiful apple
She waits patiently
As I consider its flavours
She planted the tree herself.

She says she knows a lot.
A neighbour comes around
To enquire about her strange behaviour
She reassures him
But she says that what is normal:-
Sings like the flight of swifts
And grips like a mountain
Persists like the earth
Changes like clouds
Dazzles like a sword
She continues,
The neighbour unsettled
Goes away.

She tidies the house
Of the clutter
Of many playtimes
Now she knows
That the walls were part of the game
The house has no walls.

My Sister – annotations:

'Womb, not carnivore': Hysteria – its origin many centuries ago in ancient Egypt
was thought to lie in the turbulence of the womb, which was considered as an
animal inhabiting a woman. It could crawl too near the head and had to be
attracted down by burning sweet smelling compounds – the woman squatting
over the flames – or driven upwards by something more unpleasant. Hysteria
was until relatively recently thought to be a purely female disturbance. I once
read of Freud 'seriously and earnestly considering how it was that only fifty per
cent of human kind was normal' and beginning a lecture: 'I will address the men
in the audience – as it's the other half which are the trouble.'
She responds by showing her version of life is alive and vital – she will not be
defined by his analysis. She conquers these lies that still define her playfully, by
side-stepping them lightly. M.A.W.

Your pain is mine
It's myself I help.

I see your love
But I don't desire it.

What you feel
You whom I don't know
Compels me.

So much happens
Through the magic
Of this falsehood.

Murmuring heavily
Like the call of a distant shell
You speak a name.

Will you speak my name?

Add it to the list of names
Which are carried by the sea.

Tangle me in seaweeds and corals
Tangle me.

ॐ

You who are alive

You who fight the forces of darkness
And will stop them with a painting of intense light
You with the darkness practising influences at a dis-
tance
Awash with a nightmare of knowledge
You, the desperate, doing what you can. You who
laugh
And plunge in for more with a half smile.
And you, the Mystery, who fought an army of men
With knives in the wars
The bomb fell and you nearly escaped through a
window,
My body was burnt, reduced, made new in this fire,
You the ascetic, you the sensual
You the aimless, the confused, the sensitive
You the drunk, the silent
You, we once met we shall never meet again
You who are alive,
You who teach me, sickened by the cost of my learn-
ing
I commemorate your bravery with a flower
I celebrate the insult you possess,
This body is a memory of the innocents, of the sui-
cides,
Those who dare to deceive
Not touching the ground when they fall,
This body is a charm through the deserts of the
healthy
A deception amongst deceptions; how it dances!

ॐ

Birth

Birth, the moment of tension,
The room is crowded
Waiting for brilliance

The lights are dimmed
And the sheets lie peeled back,
Concern fills the room

It is expressed in sterility
Gloves, and white masks
To prevent contamination

The machine hums, anaesthetic
Pulses, digesting movement,
The concern is heavy

It has become time
To initiate consciousness,
The first seduction,

The magic wand conjures
A rabbit from the bag
And the newborn lies, stunned

For a moment, anarchy,
The lips struggle to form meaning
Testing the possibilities

But they have no words
And the struggle disintegrates,
The meaning is forgotten

A bottle is proffered,
And the first incoherence
Dissolves in apathy.

MARBLING

The Mysterious Marbler

I remember, I remember,
Dancing with my brushes
In my obscure workshop.
Such beauty as this
Will save the world
I thought.
I remember, I remember,
The speedwells carpeting the grass
In the land by my workshop.
I remember, I remember,
How my brothers of centuries ago
Used to write the name of God
With this act.

ॐ

What are the colours of heaven?
Like marbling with pigments
Made of ground gemstones
Prepared as egg tempera,
Colours that radiate
The love which
They were created,
Such happy colours
That one might live
On the happiness
Of these surroundings.

ॐ

When I was born
The trees sighed
And wished me
The strength they had.
For with my cargo
Of words
I was fragile
On the people-ocean
Where pirates roamed.
And a royal oak
Saved me some paper
And prayed that
I would make nature new.

ॐ

SELF

Occasioned by the collapse of a house of cards.
Aged 8.

Alas my house is broken
Alas my house is dead.
With one sweep of a hurricane
My house is dead
I can stand no longer
With the wind above my head
All of it is wreckage
As the wind dies dead
I am left naked
Although the winds are dead.

I am a stranger

I am
a stranger

I live in the depths
Of a blood sky

Looking for the words
I want

I have blue eyes
I am gentle

I am breaking
Something

Because
It has stood

Looking at me
Without moving

I stand
Without moving

Looking at it
As it breaks

The dumb images
Fall unpitied

If only
They could speak

I would
Take them back

If only they
Could move

I would take
Them back

Into the blood sky
To live.

ॐ

Self

I

Eyebrows
Around the curve of their ridges

Unevenness of the skin between them.

Lip stretched up a little

The lines that skirt it,

A sheen of light
On the crest of the nose

Darkness across its bridge

Darkness on either side
Fading,

A row of short lashes
Some twisted together

From the edge of a thick lid,

Two black lines
Fused with two others,

The joins in the table

Through the door
Footsteps

II

A table
With plain legs

A drawer

Varnish,
Dull

Tiles,
Several cracked

A chair by the table
Shadow pegged down

Some coal has been piled in a heap.

A matchbox
A knife
They lie close together

The box is slightly open
At an angle to the knife

The knife is balanced
On the rim of its handle.

Through the open door
The sound of footsteps

III

Head
Tilted

Coals

Carpet on the stairs

Heels worn

Knife
Box

Eyes
Knife
Dust

One wall
Three

A tile in one corner

The texture of skin,

Warmth

IV

Looking

Looking

Rises,

Looks around

Curiously,

Thinks

ॐ

I know a man
Whose love for freedom
Was so strong
That he freed himself
From hell
And his name
Is my name.

Life hurts
On its dark side
And the spirit must leap
To cope.
Higher still and more alive
When life has passed
Death sentence;
What man may survive?
I have done.
And my name is
Marak the master
Begone all harm

Who knows what life is?
Who has lived?
Who was it that
Would give the world
Its freedom?

ॐ

Despite Anything – I

On the day that I die
I hope
I hope an eagle will weep
And carry me back
To the mountain
And I hope I will
Feel serene, lying amongst the rocks.

Close Close Close
Close your eyes
The eagle says
And be happy
That you will not return.

Despite Anything – II

All possibilities,
All futures are exhausted
But I will not remember them,
Incorporate most, in ignorance,
I will do
But I will do, nothing:
I will not be named in obscurity.

An Approach to the Threshold

AN APPROACH TO THE THRESHOLD

This is an edited version of Mark's second full-length book, a philosophical novel which examines the role of the individual in the face of war and militarism. The narrator first creates the military tank as an image of violence and then imagines various personae confronting the tank in a range of scenarios. Though written in the mid-Eighties, it has perhaps an even stronger resonance in 2004.

Mark wrote this book not long after his breakdown, and there are very strong parallels with the daily battle with fear that is often a part of living with mental illness.

I was born and I live between two wars. This is how it begins with most people. It has… always been like this.

This is not the only way, there are others. I could choose to have been born between one position of the hands of a clock and another, between two brands of custard, other, more reputable alternatives. And it is possible not to have been born and live between at all – just to be born and live. It requires reflection to live this way to the fullest. It would be curious or even ridiculous for it to be the concern of someone dying for lack of water in the desert. There is a hint of luxury or ease. It can be avoided through involvement and concentration and then through the ignorance or innocence as well as a more culpable ignorance. I have some sympathy with just living with living.

There may be some who doubt what I say through the quality of their optimism, their trusting natures. There must be those with a similar doubt which arises in their unwillingness to make assumptions. People who live after a war. Inevitability would sap me, the fear of inevitability weighs me down but the details and progress of the war are worked on and discussed every day. I find it at least useful to live as I do.

That is one reason why this war is not inevitable. It is already here, not an occasional annoyance but here all the time. Literally, because my sense of here is too limited, there is always war somewhere. Then the previous war has not ended nor the next begun, even if it is not to take place. There have been concentrations of killing. The imposition of limits gives me some sense of security. Divisions are useful if always artificial. It is a question of how war is defined. The gap seems large because it is important. In the world's history it is very little. In my concern it is almost non-existent. Perhaps this is optimistic, for it means we can tackle it without being wiped out.

I live not so much between two wars as in the phase of warfare in which we do not experience mass death. One wonders why this might be, why there is not boredom with the ritual, although I suppose that with the new weapons there is some added interest. Perhaps every generation cannot believe and has to find out for itself. Why is it not too undignified, too costly? These things seem to matter. Why? Perhaps I should be glad. There must be some idealism left or some naivety. Perhaps adventure? Individual is unreal, a fraud. Opposing groups tell us that the adventure really is. Opposing, still the purest form of adventure, is agreed on. Adventure contains a realisation of the smallest of a human being in relation to the risk they take. Something has to be found to make humankind feel small. What risk is big enough, appropriate enough? God? Existence?

I am being flippant. Perhaps it would be better not to speak at all. Between two wars there is peace. There is peace. That is more flippant still. There is peace. Recently I saw this peace. I saw men who seemed to have spent their lives feeding sweets to children. I saw how their eyes lit up at the news of a petty skirmish in which the British were involved. I saw them become tense and alert and I wondered if in the years of sweet feeding they had merely been asleep or in a trance. I think that may have been true, although as an alternative to this, I almost sympathise. Then I know someone who believes that there are wars in progress around him, which other people cannot see and in which he has fought. He is put occasionally into mental hospital for his beliefs, which probably saves him from being killed by them. There are reasons, but as for the form of the vision, it reflects something real – not war, but a source of it? It is the means of the interesting thought. But these are superficial dramatic examples of peace. A family showing friends around their new house. This is peace. They go for a picnic and eat honey sandwiches by the river. Nearby a woman in a white dress poses to advertise hair lotions. A procession passes by, headed by the mayor who is going to lay the foundation stone of a cinema. Lambs gambol. It is not enough for peace to be not obviously aggressive or non-aggressive; it must be tougher and more vibrant than that. There is war in this pleasantness. I call for a peace which is more unpleasant.

I have only partly chosen to live as I say. What convinces me is that I can feel the reality. Amongst my wider and more constant feelings, there is feeling I identify in this way. There is feeling for the times, feeling for nature, death, even the universe underlying all the turmoil and the phases of more obvious emotions. I stand on one side of the door with traffic and people. I go inside and sit in my room. The feeling is still there. These feelings are not so much heard of, not least through the difficulty of speaking of them. Their relevance or use is not obvious. Why bother, when what we know we feel is sufficient to love and hate in endless variety? They will be there whether we look for them or not and if they have purpose, will influence our involvement without requiring consciousness of them. How much more important it is to live amongst the thousand quiet ecstasies and agonies which immediately confront us.

It is in spirituality that peace and war are and are formed, as well as in actions and events. Actions are a temporary measure. Systems may subdue it, principles may lock us in and direct us to what it is that will prevent war but it is in a change in the quality of spirituality, the quality of vitality that manifests it, that the answer lies and in it a greater understanding. All that matters is feeling. There is life only because there is feeling. The world is ruled by inertia of feeling. The question of the purpose of life becomes irrelevant in feeling. It is the interest in life, without which we cannot continue to exist. The whole edifice of objects and production, transport, communication, it is only there as the expression and support of feeling. The created material world is the mere technical detail of feeling. Feelings are all that matter – these in the cataclysmic emergency of civilisation.

No doubt there will be some who will answer 'war' when the question is asked if whether peace or war is better. But really everyone believes that peace is good. But there are wars. So what is war? War is the secret held in common, more secret even than excrement. And if there is war, it follows that peace must be a secret as well. The peace which people agree to is an indulgence. We must search for the secret peace.

The meaning of peace and any other value is encoded in a thousand daily acts and gestures. It lies in the context of society, words, history but foremost it lies in the context of feeling. It is the emotional qualification which gives directives and values their true meaning, without which there are only the automata of ideology and the other amorality of habit. Values are no more than crude translations of feelings, crude reflections of hopes and fears. Values and feelings are aspects of each other. It is the spiritual which is the secret.

The meaning of values lies in history, but there is an added complication, for the feelings they express lie in history. If certain values are repeated throughout it, then feelings must be communicable, or at least broad categories of feeling, as the particular quality may change. They must be handed on, teachable. There must be a memory in society for feelings. The look which one man gives to another in the corner shop may have swept across the fertile plains of ancient Egypt. There must also be a memory for feelings in individuals if they repeat values at all in their life. One definition of a poet is someone with an unusually well-developed memory for feeling. Any feeling pursued long enough and constantly enough becomes spiritual. So what I call spiritual is not good and neurosis may become spiritual.

I would distinguish spiritual from ordinary feelings only in a few respects. All that has been felt must be there, latent, underlying other expressions but much of that feeling is for particular instances. The spiritual is a more general feeling, which is strong enough in its presence to affect the quality of more daily emotions. It is in a particular quality of feeling for life, for nature, for power and oppression, in the more basic values. It is firstly for something constant, or constant in humankind, or a section of it. And if life and nature may fail, there is God and the certainties of religious philosophies. It is the certainty from which people drew strength. But spirituality is not just an attitude conferred by religions – they are the means of limiting it to the maintenance of particular sets of values. Spirituality is an almost unavoidable attitude of people.

It is right that the spiritual has been doubted. Too often it has been a feeling for a feeling. Love! Peace! Power! It has too often been the means to ignore the world and for people to ignore themselves. In its name endless atrocities of society and relationship have been committed. Spiritualising an idea or emotion gives it great force, and intensity of any kind can resemble a will of power. It can give to an idea or feeling an absoluteness, a seeming external independent existence which is the means for people no longer to hold themselves responsible. But in tearing up the danger and idiocy of spirituality, spirituality has been torn up as well. It is something real, something useful, not an entertainment. But so much of the time it has been pursued crudely, and people speak so little about what they hold most valuable that they sometimes forget. The value of spiritual feeling is that it is the strongest and fullest realisation of value. It is the means by which peace or war are made more secure, the means through which resistance to either is most effective, the feeling which is most durable under stress. At the most general level, all spiritual feeling is about life and living.

All feeling is feeling for or against something in life. And so feeling almost always affirms life. We live to the extent that we feel, are moral only to that extent. Feeling reflects an interest in life. Spirituality is the feeling, is the interest because it is the feeling most completely about life. This interest is the feeling we have struggled towards for millennia, trying to define and to defy in external living and rules. A composer earlier this century was asked by a friend to name a higher feeling than love. He replied 'interest'. He was wrong. All feelings are forms of interest, and love is perhaps the highest form. One cannot feel uninterested; disinterested is the absence of feeling.

Depression comes about through the inadequacy, contradiction or unfulfilment of values, which are themselves expressions of feelings and fundamentally of feelings felt to be necessary to affirm life. It is an unease I call spiritual. Depression and despair reflect intense feeling and interest for life.

Strong, deep, or brilliant feeling is necessarily an affirmation of life and it is there in each person. The problem is of what is the life which is affirmed and whose life it is. There might be a person who lived to destroy humankind and who would be happy to die having accomplished that. The persistence of life might depress them. Even for this person their own life is necessary. The affirmation is of one life. With such a great vision, the glow of spirituality would be striking in their features. The feeling has not been wide enough, affirming one group at the expense of another.

War is a spiritual event. There will be many splendours of love, courage, resistance among the invasions. I hope I will have the will to resist them. I hope I will sit in a room reading a book. It is a satisfaction that technology removes the subsidiary splendours and reveals the war more purely. But there is one hope in it. It gives the opportunity to choose life or death for humankind, to emphasise that we have that absolute choice.

War is the most accessible, obvious and dramatic form of spirit. Spirit means the intensification of living through the intensification of feeling about it. War involves people living together physically and in feeling. It is a social activity. Life is concentrated to a fearful degree and as all concentration has the character of risk, the risk of living, the excitement is heightened. There is certainty and simplification to the living, the purpose has become easy, as it is the war, it is survival and it is one that can be pursued with all the certainty of grappling with a simply material world. Under these conditions, life is lived relentlessly, the spirit is lived totally, a world in itself made of fire. That the world be lived as totally is what is required of everyday life. The world of daily life has a quieter and wider complexity, more difficult to define, less brilliant and more difficult to be committed to, not least because, in this continent at least, the necessities of it are less obvious than those of war. The feeling that affirms life in peace is less obvious and less obviously necessary than the feeling which ensures it through battle. Amongst the reasons for war may be the longing for the authority of necessity and certainty.

The feeling is approached in many ways: in psychiatry, in religion, philosophies, ethics, in adjustments to relations of power and production. The war that is here is attacked at many different levels of the human, with competing claims that a particular attack will best lead the collapse to the state where life is most fully and widely affirmed. All of these have effectiveness but there is one other approach. That is to approach the feeling directly. It is possible meditation might do it. I can know the truth of the discovery only through years of practice and witnessing its results, although in anything which is not yet known there is risk; wherever there is uncertainty, there is risk. It is dangerous through this uncertainty, and alone, without the minutiae, it rules ethics, systems, actions, probably impossible to communicate, as these limit what the feeling can be. But there should be the more direct emphasis on feeling and, above all, the avoidance of stifling life by enmeshing it in etiquette. An emphasis on feeling is an emphasis on spontaneity, cutting across the immobilising knots of logical thinking.

Sometimes more ephemeral feelings can express the spirit. There is a piano concerto by Tchaikovsky in which the pianist begins by playing three simple chords one after another, the same chords in different octaves. The fingers are immobile, only the arms and body move, dropping on to the keys in an apparently simple movement, floating between three massive exclamations. It is a child's concerto! The orchestra of ninety pieces, the dimmed lighting, the hush, the knowledge and expectation of difficulty, the years of work which have gone to produce this instead of complexity and gravity, play! As if a child, confronted by a pile of wooden bricks and instructed to build a prison, throws then in the air and laughs, alive and amid the movement. There is a contradiction but it is appropriate to the circumstances. The audience still applauds. It deals with the same materials, the same gravity within the same limitations but transforms the materials in a sudden inspired movement. To have this feeling but not for a moment, perhaps for life. To contain this vitality silently without the gestures or bawling – I must fail to describe it – but feeling of this kind is what I try to live with. It is a lifetime's work.

No. No. It is too misleading. In my own delight I express too much the delightfulness of it. It took years of struggling labour to produce this freedom and it is not play, it is the triumph over difficulty. There is something tougher in this dismissal. Something darker. Even there is something sad. I have the doubt with this spirit that it is impracticable and exhausting, celebrating what cannot happen. The image doesn't illustrate the reflectiveness of the approach enough. Perhaps something stronger in beauty, more mature…

Now I will take you away to a place where I often go. At first sight it will appear to be an escape but it is not so. There are dangers. Anything can happen there, even the impossible or unlikely. I am practised at living there, or should I say 'we'? My consciousness splits into two, sometimes three or many and the resulting people are quite independent. Consequently, I shall describe myself as 'he'.

His body and shadow are surrounded by the precious soon-to-be heavy greens of early summer, which he has had the luxury of blocking out. Other, equally precious colours dot the short grasses. By a not uncommon freak of nature, special climate, infrequent visiting and the right winds, a slightly exotic collection of flowers has concentrated on the ground he has chosen. They sit as clearly and completely as illustrations from an old botanical handbook. And miraculously, a tulip grows not far from his head. Despite their originality, the effect overall is of gentleness, of naturalness and of calm. No doubt the open-eyed inhabitants of cities dream of such a place as this, or with a fence, or a fence around the tulip, or preferring more humans or convenient entertainment, it remains as a fleeting thought. In this place he lies.

He lies looking open-eyed but at the sky, reasoning relentlessly against a blue background of which he is unaware, or the play of light and cloud infect this thinking. His thinking originated there perhaps, from an identity of thinking and sky. He made it the basic assumption.

One of his hands tears grasses from beside his body, moistening its fingers with their juices, disrupting the apparent formality of his layout. He lies with the neatness of an upright man in a queue. He must be quite confident to lie like that. He lies at the centre of a small plateau.

Beyond the edges of the plateau, birds move slowly within the vastness of the sky. There is an abundance of birds. There is an abundance of moving objects which represent them: they move amongst themselves and the sky as specks of dust disturbed by its currents. What causes this abundance? The vastness and clarity of the sky. It is these qualities which make them seem so many and, with the many, a further quality, the something akin to joy at being in the sky. To joy, to possessiveness – helplessly they move there, impelled in their daring. These are possibilities hidden by distance. Almost, there is only a teeming or a swarming of birds. The sky is rich in birds.

Above the plateau the sky is free, emptying on to the ground and continuing in it. Sun, sky and grass involve each other in the virtuosity of growing. Little diverts from the securing of the one element to the other, the concentration of sky and grass. The whole activity operates in stillness.

Although the plateau is open to light and is light, it is dark beside the intensity of the sky and the inequality is reinforced by the blurred shadows of its surface. These give the position of its dips and gullies, which are more frequent towards the circumference of the plateau and which seem, brokenly, to form a pattern. A bird flies across the plateau, flying unswervingly with the slow undulation and the noiselessness of an owl. Sunlight reflects from its back.

Suddenly the clouds! As if thrown by a spinning child, suddenly the clouds, in each moment suddenly. Traversing the sky in a gigantic circling movement, like the gashes the plough has made, their parallel rows pass into the distance. The sky breaks against the clouds, sunlight catching their crests, dissolving in them, discolouring them. The sky breaks, one row, each row, again and again.

Amongst the grasses a stray leaf quivers, upright in a hole, tugged, probably by a worm. Throughout the maze of greenstuff, hundreds of similar scenes will be enacted. His face muscles tauten: a sneer, a look of suspicion which remains, fading slowly. Away from him the grass is longer, without the meticulous grazing of his immediate surround. Gently, through the strains of growth, a grass blade springs from under another which restrained it. He becomes restless, uncomfortable and rolls over. With difficulty he props himself on one elbow and looks at the ground on which he has been lying. He examines the impression of his body attentively. He feels the impression and smiles. A corner of his mouth twists. Absently he picks out an area of grass and finds the soil beneath it.

He flops back to the ground with an exasperated sigh. His expression is indefinite enough to suggest several kinds of feeling but there is a rigidity which rules out boredom or sleep. His face awaits a feeling. He awaits something. After a short time he shuts his eyes, confirming at least that there has been a feeling. He lies in the sun but a noise breaks the stillness, a vibrating, a cracking, an indistinct noise. He reopens his eyes and looks around, puzzled, finding no source for it. He stops still to catch it more clearly. The noise breaks off. It re-continues, different in pitch. It is a buzzing. He has seen a large-winged insect close to him. He watches it. Again he lies down.

His position and the other peculiarities of the ground around him emphasise his intrusion on the plateau. He treats it as a large bed or, since he is conscious, as a psychiatrist's couch, although it has more of a bed like comfort. His need of such space can be questioned. Possibly he is protecting himself against disturbance. As he seems not to take much notice of his luxury, it could be power, although familiarity would also explain it.

Over the lip of the plateau, a man climbs into view. He turns and looks back into the sky, resting. He is dressed in well-worn clothing, loose-fitting and faded as if he might be a farmer or farm labourer, and the weight of one arm is supported by a stick. A gentle breeze now plays over the ground, almost imperceptibly it drifts, one way then another. The man fills his lungs with the air in a private appreciation of it. Having stood for a few moments he turns in to the plateau and takes a few steps. But then, only briefly pausing, he retraces his steps and disappears. His leaving coincides with a laughter which would have been audible at the distance which separates the two men.

As well as this intrusion, there are signs on the plateau of other disturbances and of occurrences not immediately apparent from its centre. In the indentations of the ground there are, occasionally, pieces of paper and plastic wrapping which have caught there, transported by the wind. A cigarette butt, other oddments of rubbish, discoloured by their length of stay, a charred area where there has been a fire, sheltered from the wind. These more certainly indicate a previous occupation and, as the result of some senseless mowing, grass lines the bottoms of the snaking gullies which cross the plateau, probably scythed for fodder but left. This is not unlikely because a sunken track, marked freshly by the treads of a heavy vehicle, cuts directly through the plateau. More gently, there are the signs of wildlife, the holes made here are there by a small mammal and, on searching amongst the grasses, the minute partings and flattenings of the regular runs.

The man's eyes are shut but he seems more aware of his circumstances, to have stopped thinking as a pleasant smile freshens his face. He stretches his limbs and allows them to collapse. 'Ah! One could drown in this warmth,' he murmurs and he surrenders himself to a unity with his surroundings. He surrenders the minute alienation that comes through consciousness, floating there as a being, no longer an effigy. With the release he seems younger; released from thought, released also from the emotions which motivate thought, and so younger. In this younger face, the wrinkles at the corners of the eyes come from a straightforward humour, one without irony and may have originated in facing the sun.

He looks fixedly. The grass, clouds, sky: he sees them as frozen in the course of movement, which is to say that he sees them intensely and as intense, poised for resolution. In his looking he is not completely relaxed. There is something of the relationship of cat and mouse. He is at play with this scene. So, above it, yet he participates and his humour is directed partly at himself, at his relationship with this nature of which he is fond. Strictly, what goes on around him is pointless and he is ambivalent in his attitude to it. It is good with a goodness he feels despite himself. He smiles at himself for this weakness, for this release from responsibility. He smiles because he can feel Good.

He only has eyes for that which is original. What is not good, the varieties of litter and other intrusions, he does not see. Probably, if he were to, he would laugh. 'Good. It is beautiful. The world will be saved by beauty.' He cuts short the last word with a pained expression. 'Why can't I take it seriously?' And he seems genuinely sad. 'It is good. Good for…morale. I'm on holiday.'

He turns and sets off to leave the plateau. After the first steps his arms begin to swing, his stride lengthens and his feet spring lightly from the turf. He walks uninterrupted across a less wrinkled surface of the plateau. Arriving at its edge, he follows it towards a knot of small, velvet-textured hills which extend at a lower level.

Far below where he walks is a great plain, virtually treeless and divided into fields. Roads and tracks further organise the plain and along them farm buildings, generally whitewashed, reflect the mellow light of the early evening sun. Villages are scattered throughout the plain, concentrated at the intersections of the roads. Distantly, there is a town. Suspending all movement, even that of breath, it is just possible to hear the sounds of cattle, although more as an irregular imperfection of the silence than as distinct sound. Listening carefully, there are centuries of this lowing. Obscure nomadic migrations occupy the plain, thousand strong herds shake the earth, bells jangling. The settlement is little obstruction to them. It shares the same obscurity. From this height there is a feeling of unreality. It seems that the people who live there must live a waking dream. There are no questions in this landscape. This, then, is life. This noiseless teeming, these dazed outcrops without mess.

It is evening. The blue of the sky is diluted in the approaching darkness and mottled with other tints. It has become more transparent, less overwhelming than it was, easing its grasping of reality. Gracefully the blue sky collapses, dispensed with. A few birds cling to it, drugged by the holiday of nature there has been. Amongst the hills it is darker still. There is less that is obvious and the darkness intensifies a dull metallic sound which comes from them. There is an activity. The activity is one which takes place in darkness.

On the side of a hill a conical structure is silhouetted against the sky. By the light of a fire nearby a man moves busily, his face illuminated, reddened and gleaming in the firelight. His clothing merges with the darkness. He may be wearing robes or a monk's habit. The base of the structure has been smashed open and a glowing, fuming mass is exposed. With tongs in one hand he removes a putty-like substance and carries it almost running to the fireside. There, on an anvil, he attacks it with a hammer, turning it this way and that, shaping it, expelling flecks of a granular material; in the same rhythm of movement he casts it on to a pile of finished work in a handcart.

Around him are other similarly tapering structures of all sizes and curvatures. Some are cracked or fallen in, others smoke. The angular shapes of a solid machinery are just visible in the gloom. He hurries amongst the constructions, tending to their various requirements. At the first he leaves the handcart and, taking up a long rod, knocks out the bricks which block its entrance. Minutes later, a glowing vessel stands on the earth into which he peers. The contents satisfy him. He nods his head. He begins to move swiftly. Red-hot crucibles pass in and out of the furnace, returning filled with the contents of his handcart and small lumps of a light, black substance. He wears few clothes. The muscles churn in his back and arms. Perspiration runs down his shaven head. At last he stands back, looking at the sealed furnace.

Spitting on his hands he moves reluctantly to a pile of ingots, with which he loads the cart. He braces himself. He has to yoke himself to move it. The outline of his body shows the effort he makes as the load is hauled, creaking, to another furnace. He relieves himself of it, as if driven by a sudden pain, staggering, flexing his back. Some torches burn with a dense smoke. Taking one, he clambers inside the furnace. In it is a pit filled by a stone chest, well illuminated by the reflection of light from the glazed walls of the chamber. This he begins to charge with ingots, alternately layered with the charcoal. He is everywhere amongst the furnaces, working bellows, hammering, operating machinery, struggling. The night stretches on. Red-hot oblongs move in the night, elongating as they move. The night gives him energy, concentrates his attention, exciting it by its discolours of fire. He would take some of this darkness with him into daylight.

The components are completed. These he spreads out in the sun ready for assembly. They occupy a large area. The requirement is increased by the machines, jigs and pulleys which are needed to manipulate them. Tinted goggles are worn for the initial work, then follow eyepieces, even microscopes and sophisticated machinery to measure what the eye cannot see. In order to feel the fullest weight of a particular association, the fabrication takes place in the open air. Flowering rye grass pokes through the holes in a metal slab. Sunlight dazzles on the concave mirror of a lamp. It is more healthy to work in these conditions. One can feel that one is alive. In the breaks from work there are strolls in the hills and, once in a while, camomile to make tea from. As well, there is less disturbance, no overseer. Relaxed, it is pleasant to run a hand over the work and reflect on it, admire the quality of the patina. And the sky is there as choice. There is the option there would not normally be.

I opt for work. I involve myself. Then, the metal pieces are more certain, more easy to grapple with than the sky. It seems dull but one must sin a little. In the next job I do some welding. I have already set up the equipment I need. It is not difficult but I have to climb up to reach the spot. There is a casting like an egg sliced down its length with a bulge in the short end and a hole at the other. Parallel with its section, another slices through the egg. I have to weld a flat plate to the hole which is facing the sky. The bottom rim of the casting rests on a platform on which I also stand. I take up some rods I have by me.

Gun barrels lay discoloured by the heat to blues and reds. The ground was littered with metal. All round there were fragments. He picked his way indifferently through the remains of the wood. He walked on. His feet pulverised what they touched. In the distance there were noises; here, quiet, charcoal and metal. At the edge of the wood he stopped. He stopped completely, still in the motion of walking. A noise entered the stillness. Slowly he lifted his head. A tank climbed the rise. He walked out on to the flat ground.

It drove directly at him. He looked at it. He looked beyond it. His arms hung loosely by his sides. The tank checked in its movement. It re-continued at the same speed. His hands clenched. His eyes begin to water. Suddenly within a few yards of him the tank pulled up, edging forward. He gasped, his eyes stared. His face shook, rigid with passion. Tears ran down his face. A hatch in the tank's turrets opened and the commander stood up, looking enviously at the man in front. He shouted an order. The tank stopped. Its engines were shut off. The man lifted his eyes to the turret. The commander took a breath, about to shout. Instead, he studied the face. He looked up. Then, noiselessly, he climbed down from the tank and sat to one side, looking at the man. The man stood where he was, shaking. He turned his head towards the commander. In a brisk movement the commander rapped on the hull and ordered the crew out. They came out. One man started to laugh. He stopped abruptly. They sat down and looked, alternately at the man and at the ground. They sat for minutes. The man's expression remained unchanged. One of the crew stood and walked to him. They faced each other at close quarters. Suddenly they seized each other. There was hatred in their tears.

And now I will show you this work of mine, not perfect, a bit of a jumble but there is plenty of time. It works as well as any other and that is the main thing. You know I took it snorkelling yesterday. Tanks snorkel! That's the least of it. And afterwards we have a cup of tea. We call it 'having a brew up'. Tanks make fine tea, almost human. One has to laugh.

The turret you know about, well, no. There are two hatches in it. They are really both cupolas in this tank, upside-down cups. One has nine periscopes around it, the other rather fewer. Both rotate and have contrarotation facilities for alignment of the main armament with the commander's sight. On top of the right hand hatch is an AAMG (that is, an anti-aeroplane machine-gun) and below it another MG which can be fired from inside. There are co-axial 7.62s on both sides of the main armament which is 100mm smooth bore, with a thermal sleeve to protect against barrel bend. It fires squash-heads, fin-stabilised, heat-seeking – all ammunitions. All ammunition is stored in pressurised water containers, especially on the right-hand side of the driver, who sometimes sits on the left, or in the middle. An escape hatch connects the fighting and driver's compartment. The driver has a gun too, sometimes. There is all the trickery I won't go into now, devices to see at night and navigate under water, computers, radar, lasers. With all this there is talk of redundancy, one man less – in some cases. Who'd want to be fired from a tank! Who'd want to stay? It gets very smelly. There is ventilation, the fume extractor in the gun is invaluable, but it's so cramped, not pleasant. You can understand; the men must stay there a long time.

On the outside you can see the excellent ballistic design, the sloped glacis plate at the front, the turret, the whole thing as close to the ground as is practicable. It runs on six pairs of road wheels – one doesn't normally think of tanks having wheels. Five of them have traverse torsion suspension and the sixth just a pack of springs. In the old days a tank ride used to be quite a shake-up. The speed is a compromise. On the one hand, the need to push onwards fighting on the move, on the other, limitation through the heavier armour needed in pitched battles. For both we need smoke, plenty of smoke. Vaporised fuel mixes with the exhaust. Forward cover is through smoke grenades from launchers at the side of the turret. A battle wouldn't be a battle without smoke. And the crew compartment seals under pressure. There are air filters and respirators.

So why a tank? Why a city? What is it? In one city it is dark; sequinned figures dart like electricity amongst the buildings. In one city they walk with purpose. In one city they go to work and have neighbours. In one city people shout. What goes on around the corner? In those buildings, surely there is some power? It is the city of large black cars. It is the city where people die. Why do people die?

When the city stank and children lived on the streets, when it burned to the ground, when bombs excited it, when all these things were and more there was a point in dying. They struggled and fought stupidly for this death. And when the fire, the explosions, the stink, when they were not transformed but merely hidden away and perfumed, the people wandered about aimlessly. Dying had become pointless. People died in a state of soundless shock, wondering what had happened. And with the dying, the living became more difficult. There were just vague threats.

It is easy to die in front of a tank. It is probable. It is easy to live there. People do live there. People live more intensely there, that is the attraction – the concentration of living, its clarification and simplification.

Where death and life are put so close together, life is the closest and so the spirit. The spirit is accessible. The tank is assessable. It can be touched. Still, it is too ideal. I would rather put there a man, or liquids gurgling in each other. The tank is a compromise, less attractive to mystery.

I use a tank because of its triteness, its cleanliness, the sophistication that surrounds its simple mechanical functions because it is not evil. It is trite in the way it kills. It is the triteness which kills. It is a machine of 'yes' or 'no'. I use it because, as a reduction of all this city, it is trite, like sliced meat on a plate, controversial in its crudity, so I can laugh at it, laughing with the knowledge that it can kill. I can despair. Then I am choosing it because it misleads me with the superficiality. If I am led to find it too easy to protest against, it will kill me. If I don't protest it will kill me. There are many risks in confronting the tank. One has to know its precise nature. Already it is not so trite. There is a great deal that the tank, as the city, can be. I do not feel superior to it. So I stand in front of a tank.

I have a thought that to stop the tank will require unusual feelings, though ones which must be there, in part, in my motivation. I think it is requiring stronger feelings than usual. I cry for the world to be stronger and more 'inhuman' than it is found to be! I would like to decriminalise feeling. I would like to criminalise everyday life. Already I practise a crime. It is the crime of deceit. I am immersed in untruth.

I lead a vicarious existence. Everywhere there is a tank I am there and everywhere I am there is a tank. My immersion enforces a ubiquity. This has its strain, not to say claustrophobia. I hope that the variety will save me, although it may merely be more dangerous through increasing my insubstantiality. I must watch but I am not a fool. Sometimes I go and lie in the sun. I go and look at other visions, with more simple beauties. They are important as well. I would like to incite wonder as well as disaffection. Then there are practical considerations to take me out of myself.

If the tank is under bombardment and advancing in battle, the appearance of a man in front of it will be unlikely to have any unusual effect. There are sensible tactical considerations of when and where. But even in this example, the answer is not obvious, the answer to the question of a man. When the whole attempt is not the attempt of something sensible, the most unlikely occurrences are relatively less unlikely. I think people must be stupid. I cultivate stupidity. For example, the appearance of an unarmed man in front of the tank in that situation could be valuable in its surprise. The battle could emphasise the contrast of peace and war. There is a chance of the tank crew being overwhelmed by the daring of appearing in this circumstance. Their bravery, or at least pursuit of it, would make them appreciate the opposing quality of bravery and be puzzled by the alternative. This is a general consideration in my action, for them to see themselves as outcompeted in their own terms. I require them to be brave. The terms reconstitute subtly but there is too much against this, wonderful as it would be if it happened. I cannot rely on miracles. Under the conditions of battle they have placed themselves in a position where they must kill or die. With their fear – and there is only bravery when there is fear – with their absorption in their drive to accomplish, they are hardly likely to stop for me, even if they sympathise. It might give them something to reflect on afterwards – and after reflection? Even so, it is beside the point for me to die, it is inefficient. There is a sense in which I must die in order to confront, and in success there is a death; but the point is primarily for me, and us, to live…. Whatever the likelihoods, I consider the possibilities. In the event I may be overtaken by surprise, so I cultivate flexibility.

Has the tank recently been attacked? The crew are relieved to be alive, just dazed, just holding on to control, subdued. My appearance is less of a shock but sympathy is far from their minds. They understand, apathetically. Their minds are full of fire and smoke, the reality fills them, they don't see how life can be otherwise. They have neither the energy to agree to my challenge, nor even to argue with it. They move me aside in silence. There is bitterness.

Or, they leave the tank without emotion. We do not embrace. We walk without either hope or hopelessness. There is nothing else to be done. In this scene there is a better chance of being listened to, or at least of getting a reaction, as the bitterness might take the form of revenge, a real threat. They hate me as they hate humankind or themselves, or they have contempt for those outside their reality. This is a worry, whether I will be recognised as being in the same reality.

The tank has been hit. They celebrate, happy to be alive. Seeing me, they are quiet. They listen seriously and with warmth. In their survival they have life more than they ever had before. They know something of what it can mean. It is possible, but they may see me as a killjoy. They may see me as an intruder, an outsider to their shared experience. They may be high-spirited with bravado and mockingly lead me off by one ear or a kick to the backside. They may pull me in to go and get drunk with them. It must not be too easy for them to stop. Beside the choice of avoidance, there must be the choice of killing. The crew must be in a state where they choose.

The tank has had varying degrees of involvement. Varying qualities of involvement. The crew are from units variously dedicated. They are in varying degrees battle-hindered. They have recently attacked, with success, with partial success. Retreat. Atrocities are planned. The tank is in a conquering conflict. It is in a defensive conflict. Justification on the nation scale.

I can know all of these factors and I examine the range of their effects. He is entered amongst these complications, each time freshly, as if for the first time. That his freshness is my own keeps me in reasonable health but there is sheer physical fatigue, perpetual concern with surfaces; with the physical, an impregnable factualness which I bloody my hands against, tearing at the enigma of the tank, trying to understand and communicate with this metal through which so much converges. I doubt. I detect a falsity in my doubt which glorifies the difficulty of what I do. Hating them, I doubt, wondering if the hatred is also false. It is important for my success to be honest. On one occasion, as we embrace, my spine is severed by the small knife which he had in his sleeve. He laughs, not unkindly, and shakes his head. 'You were so naïve.'

I return to the tank, clean it and oil the moving parts. The cakes of mud are levered off its tracks and while I am at this level, I notice a space beneath its hull which leaves room for a body to crawl. I smile. I clean it but don't polish it: the polished surface would reflect sunlight and give away its position too easily. I check that everything works as was intended. Standing off and looking, moving back in to it, I have the feeling of being a sculptor. Slowly I work at it, content in the work. Only when I stop can I worry. Only when it is complete can I be sure, even of failure.

I decide to dress differently. First there is a battledress, apparently belonging to one side. One brand of tank would stop but what about the response? Arrest is a strong probability. To be seen as a tiresome fool, an encumbrance, perhaps a coward, perhaps sent to the doctor as a sufferer from battle fatigue and locked inside a tank for a few days. There is no cause for the same tension. Later the crew might say, well, yes, he's got a point. I have to argue, so speak familiarly, as here they see me as a man. Perhaps there has been a movement of disaffection. They will recognise me better and take me more seriously, react against me more violently, as what I pose seems more feasible. As an individual I would be tolerated. Toleration is the enforcement of banality, it is amongst my worst enemies.

Against another army, there is still the advantage of my protesting from within the same world, of being recognised as part of it and eliciting a certain minimal respect, and there would probably be a greater weight of significance attached to my presence. The question it would raise would be more charged than in the previous case. I could be a deserter. But why stand in front of a tank? They might not notice that I was doing that. There could be a trap. I would have to choose the position carefully. Of course, they might well shoot me as they saw me in the distance. Position again, something about the way I stand. If I were quite still or walked towards them? They think I am a robot, they mistake me for a charity collector. They shoot me without thinking too much but I would think that either before or after the event there would certainly be curiosity.

If I were to dress in saffron robes, what I meant would be quite apparent but, even understood, would there be the same force of statement? I would be taking less risk and I would be an outsider. In all probability my option would have been a source of amusement in civilian life. Is not there too much symbol and not enough human? No, I can see some chance. The soldiers follow me, bewildered, surprised at themselves. I am not sure. I am, anyway, not sure that I have an option beyond a battledress.

Hosts of people are wasted before the tank, nuances of a person. There is a sense in which the action is too important to be left to an individual. It is not surprising that I sometimes feel myself as an impresario, sometimes as the footman announcing guests at a ball. I place great importance on my subjects. However, the unspoken reservations I might have had in these positions are lost in the confusion. The laughter which this provokes can itself be too professional. I subject my efforts to the test of laughter, gauging their accuracy by the quality of it. These pretensions reflect a genuine striving but they are not tough or appropriate enough in the event and they will not stand up to it. At times angry, I try to deal gently with these minor idealisms, be patient with them, as they cannot be allowed to divert me to a disturbance. Constantly, though, there is the worry that my most distant reflection is not free from this mistake. With so much repetition, or more accurately near repetition (as at least one of me is changed), spontaneity becomes a problem. I am left with the amorality of habit. I have to approach the tank with knowledge, yes, I cannot deny myself that, but as if I had never actually done so before. I have again to grasp that the tank is actually there. To remedy this requires of me a certain kind of forgetfulness, which I find hard to describe – emptyheaded, just potential, a mind that is alert in a state of concentration.

Here is another of the pitfalls. There has always been a temptation for me to play and rejoice in the colours and sounds. Unnecessary decorative or symbolic flourishes become attached, tending to ritualise the event or make a pageantry of it. For a long time a white butterfly persisted in flying across the battlefield, unconcerned as a cat. How I hated that sentimentality. How I hated the mischievousness! Enraged I stormed, looking for the culprit. Almost, I threw a brick at the insect. It wouldn't go away. Eventually, I found that I was fond of it and left it in peace. Through greater concentration I have become either free from it or blind to it. I don't know which. For all I know, it is still there.

These errors can be expressed as an error in what I am posing to the tank. In a way they are errors in sincerity. In a way, because an actor will be sincere towards the part they play. There is a danger of superficiality. It is possible to die even for the pursuit of a counterfeit sincerity. For the time being there is an element of insincerity. I am unaware of the degree but I know that I cannot actually approach the tank without generally having lived the protest beyond what my sporadic discipline managed to hold for moments. I must be as I imagine. That does not mean that I am pure. The feelings may be complex, my cynicism may be sincere. A dictator may torture sincerely, morally. It is an elusive quality. To put it another way, the tank disintegrates as I approach sincerity in protest and that is my estimate of it. The sculptor destroys the sculpture, chips away to reveal another shape, perhaps a donkey, or to reveal nothing at all. In the face of death, my expression will be sincere. At least then I will feel for the world something my thinking reveals me as lacking. So I pose a statement? A desire, a longing, a command, a request?

This has led me to the question of who I am. Ah! I am someone, that is all. Here though, I have a choice. The link between freedom and imagination is strong. If I am young I may indicate passion, I may indicate thoughtlessness. If I am old, respect, but a feeling that I no longer understand the present world. If I am a child, the tank probably stops – but what then? I cannot ask a question in the fullest knowledge, in my expression I cannot explain. I have decided that I must be old enough for the world to have entered my features, then perhaps implying better that I know what I do. Old enough to realise how short the centuries are and how little time is left. Old enough to have doubted material ambitions and the more straightforward preferences of youth. This is not a chronological age. There must be in my uncertainty something of the quality of old age's doubts. There must also be some rashness, although it will have some of the quality of an old man's rashness, knowing most richly that there is little more to lose and bearing that explanation engrained on my face. The child is there. To do this is impossible without the child. It would take many hours to show the range of considerations. But hypothesising would be an accurate description. The face that screams by a tank knows the world through living it.

Since the dawn of time… a deep urge has driven him to enhance proficiency at arms by the improvement of his weapons. While first thought sufficient… or simply with bare hands… soon… protection against hostile weapons… More swiftly… nimbly…Thus…an interest in armoured fighting vehicles… from the third millennium. The celebrated standard of Ur… vehicles drawn by beasts… armed men… hides… dust.

The book lies open on the table. No further reading of it is necessary. He pushes himself up and walks to the bookshelves to find the particular book which may explain further. His walk is slow and troubled, weighted with the victims of the past who tread in his steps, wanting also to know. He takes the book, sits down and opens it. He reads a story which was first recorded in the city of Ur, which means first.

I will proclaim to the world the deeds of Gilgamesh. He was wise. He saw mysteries and secret things… The great gods made his beauty perfect, surpassing all others, terrifying like a great wild bull. Two thirds they made him god, one third man. In Uruk he built walls. Look at it still today… Touch the threshold, it is ancient… Regard the foundation terrace. Is it not burnt brick and good? The seven sages laid the foundations. He seized the herb of youth from the bottom of a stream. The herb was eaten by a serpent as he slept.

He reads the prologue, then sits back. The smile fades momentarily as he sees the city of Uruk before his eyes, with its gold-topped battlements, its people who walk unstopped. The eagle which floats in the clear sky beyond its walls. The paper, the room, become visible through the landscape. The vision dematerialises, leaving surprise at its absence, the echo of it continuing into silence. The book is distant upon the table. He speaks.

Two thirds god, two thirds, I cannot see him. Here I am lonely. I am lonely because of Gilgamesh. He is remote. It is difficult to speak to him because speech is not his expression: as one third human, his language is only one third so. It was in recognition of his problem with language that the gods made him a companion, Engkidu, covered with long hair, living with the antelope herds. Were the gods playing a joke to make immortality so close? But it was these two thirds which built the city, the two thirds that made it seem that things might be better, the ghost of the two thirds which has gone into…this. We live on the threshold of the same city. And what is Gilgamesh, not who, what is he? He is a tank, two thirds metal and high explosive, one third man. Yes, here is the tank.

There is a word I must speak. The cautiousness with which I approach this word. It has many meanings. The word 'man'. Gilgamesh was a man in the aspect of man's most majestic futility. Cautious in saying the word man, I am even more cautious in saying 'woman'. There is an explosiveness in both these words. I have been concerned with the problem of how to stop a tank by posing it the question of a man, by posing this question to men. There have been women with me, although they seemed just to be there. I have not asked. Sometimes there are people whose faces are indistinct but one I know has been the face of a woman. Through male tradition the crew of the tank would be more likely to be puzzled at her presence there, less likely to assume that she had violent intentions, more easily reminded of values they held dear, but would they be convinced? They might follow her. It depends on the basis of their stopping. There is a tradition of cars stopping to let women cross the road. Then, they might simply stop through the same embarrassment which would have caused them to break off telling a bawdy joke in her presence. Why am I a man? It is because men fight wars, cause wars. It is because I can know this suffering most fully. If only I can become aware of it. With a man, the contradiction is greater.

Consider a symbol – isn't it like a human? There is something material representing something material. There is something unseen, like a halo, an aura, through which the material is radiant. There is a root called a mandrake which grows in the earth below a gallows and which represents in form a human. All symbols are mandrakes. Now consider again the confrontation. It is a confrontation of symbols. Two man-gods confront each other in their fullest mystery, since, as an alternative, I too am a symbol. I am a man, in the fullest sense I can allow and representing myself in that sense. Opposing is another sense and this sense in one sense therefore plays out my ambivalence. The tank moves slowly or it has stopped. Largely it is a sense in which the tank either rusts or falls apart. I have some optimism, or no, I am being realistic, I am already in something of this relationship. This is one threshold, the threshold which divides me from myself. Another, similar to the first is the division between myself and other people, another, between myself and women. This position, this confrontation, is the position of humankind. Continually, through symbol, I act out the larger drama. I act out the drama of love, for our hesitation before each other is the agonising before the relief of commitment. The same is repeated. Different, increasingly richer individuals collapse or fade, merge to re-enter the higher phase. Beyond symbol, through the tank, may be what I actually confront. I cannot rule it out.

So I stare out, a human agony caged in symbol, like a man on fire. It has been done before I am tempting suicide. With me others burn, witches, heretics, all the classes of people who burn. What will I take with me? What are my final wishes?

Music. I will take music and play a jig – but a special kind of music. Only music has an accuracy of definition, evokes with least necessity of material association, least reduction, as there is little it specifically claims to represent. That is why I choose music – what it presents, it presents completely. What I take with me must be music. Overall this music will be what is worth stopping for.

Let me take as an example the final movement of Beethoven's Choral Symphony, the Ode to Joy. Sometimes this music reminds me of carthorses careering in a field, or a pub song, the men beating time on the tables with their fists. A sprawling, crude joy, crushing others not in the same mood. This is some of the force, its power to upset gentility and inhibition. I can see it as a joy which has no bearing on the world. Look up and see an ageing man shouting a grandiose, ideal joy, almost blind, bumping into lampposts and pedestrians, laughing at his naivety. Then it is pompous in a more oppressive way, claiming obedience to itself. But what else? It is inconsistent with reality but it is inconsistent in some quite useful ways. It is inconsistent with well-groomed facades, slick advertising, clean smooth progress – another composer in the last century complained that 'Beethoven tells us too much. He tells us about the pain in his soul but then he tells us about the pain in his bowels.' It is a joy which has been grasped certainly, daring, there is strength in it. On occasion I have laughed, not with the joy but with a delight at it, surprised by its simplicity and newness, at something so immense being delivered so confidently and easily. Of course, I can feel it as beautiful, excitingly beautiful, affecting me even physically, a kind of tension – living is a tension – I shiver. I feel goose pimples spread over my body. When I leave the concert-hall, though, and a drunk knocks me down and jeers, how does the experience stand up to this? There is a vulnerability in the music, a gentleness not immediately apparent, and with it I feel a sadness common in experiencing beauty, best expressed in the wondering question of 'How can this be so?' Simply by itself there is too much which this music is not inconsistent with. It was not felt to be inconsistent with National Socialism, its heroism perhaps too wide and universally applicable to exclude this.

I play this music to the tank. Music is traditionally a soother and healer. What effect will it have? If it is listened to in the same way as in the concert hall, destruction is out of the question, and any piece of music would fulfil this function. This is an added qualification to the slowness and stillness of time in which I try to isolate the tank, this quality of listening. The context influences the meaning, so in me, in bearing the music in this particular relationship, I may exclude some unwanted associations.

The music is insubstantial in that the roar of motors and explosions may physically drown the sound without destroying it. A composer in the early part of this century whispered murderously on his deathbed that he would 'take it back' – take back the Choral Symphony. It has sometimes to use the appearances of being stranded – like a whale on the mud-banks of this century – but I don't think it is altogether possible to 'take back'. It has been unleashed so it is there. It must still be there – as anything an individual has experienced, so with history. Through the insubstantiality I present the tank with immortality, a true immortality, which I hope it will grasp. The tank will stop to listen.

As an accompaniment to the tank's progress there is too much ambiguity. It is music with which to hug another man in a crushing embrace. Then I can also see that a man might kill with the same intoxicated exuberance. He might in this state be too abstracted to see the aspect of horror and obscenity in killing, seeing the victims not as individuals but as part of a joy, a titanic struggling, cleansing its foetidness. Warriors have often gone into battle happy, reckless.

There is music I can set alongside war without this risk, Indian sitar music for example, but the relevance of that is too distant, too easily ignored. I think of Bach's Saint Matthew Passion. It is music of the world of humankind, not to one side or in a still, well-lit room. It deals with humankind more completely. I have heard it alongside images of the Warsaw ghetto and it did not seem out of place, not entertaining, not luxurious or privileged. It seems to me to deal with what took place. It expressed the agony, not as a scream but along with the strength to withstand. A humanity which tears itself apart in an effort to overcome its tearing itself apart. It deals not only with the obviously oppressed and so it expresses the tragedy of humankind and the determination to overcome itself. Inside the tank I am not too sure; there is no call to action in the music, it is an accompaniment. They might kill with this music, feeling the heaviness and tragedy but resigned to it.

So I combine this music with the previous one, this more considered view with the reckless joy: with each piece in the context of the other, the music loses some of its ambivalence. The statement/demand/plea/description… It begins to take shape, further defined in meaning by the circumstances in which it is heard and by whom it is heard.

I continue. Much other music will be there, music-hall songs for the comradeship and earthiness. Jazz, blues, particular pieces which seem to me to have valuable aspects, the volume of each music adjusted according to the value I consider it to have.

I am not a music box, or a maker of music boxes, more like a composer, grasping these sounds, this sound, as if originating in me. How is it to discover the Choral Symphony in one's head, walking down the street? Beyond the composer I am a decomposer, a rotter of sounds. Through this composition, through having originated it I seek what is most important, its origin in myself. It boils and bubbles, gives off pungent vapours. I return to it now and then. Each time it is quieter as we near the origin. Like the game of musical chairs, there may only be action when the music stops, like perhaps this society. In a sense I long for the time when all that can be heard is the sound of its breathing. It is my silence that will confront the tank, a silence in which there is implicit: my composition, the harmonising, the counterpointing of all the sounds of the world, the harmony which is one great distance, more like the clashing chord which immediately proceeds the Ode of Joy. Yes! That was the real music and what shall I call it? There is no need of a name. It is the shriek of the living, for we must be most alive to sing.

If all the known objects of the universe were taken and thrown into random motion, what would there be? Randomness? There would be the confusion of randomness, but the whole? It is a picture of human limitation. It is an event which says not 'universe' but 'humankind'. Even this cosmic event is a symbolism. With less than complete knowledge one is reduced to symbolism. It is a necessary state of existence. The totality would mean everything, or nothing. Even to perceive the totality means 'I'. Only less than complete knowledge is meaningful. One is reduced to convention because symbolism is convention; only conventions are communicable. And this is my problem.

What exactly is it that I take with me? How wide is the totality I represent? How far beyond myself in knowledge must I go? To put in front of the tank a civilisation is to tempt it in the extreme: few times have so few had the opportunity to accomplish something so great, so easily, and civilisations have little feeling or pathos which can be respected. Rather that civilisation in the aspect of a man, I put there a man in the aspect of civilisation. I will not go so far beyond myself. I put there a picture of the world. I put there the reality in which we are at that moment engaged, through having most fully discovered it in me. I go there as aware. I put there what is risked. I put there what might be and what might be thrown away. I stand as a dervish, spinning to the accompaniment of gongs, one hand pointing to the earth, the other to the sky, in between, a human. Beneath the robes and the pointed hat of a prophet, the eyes of a man.

I am symbol but I am an imagined symbol. I am as I imagine, presenting the tank with something unknown, unrealised. I present it with the future. All communicable symbols deal with a past which is known. As I must communicate, I must present it with a past which is not known, the past which the Past has woven around and touched but kept secret. I present it with the future, for the calamity which may take place is not the future, being already known. It is the meeting of past and future, symbol and imagination, impossible and possible………..

Alone in my room with its knife and box at an angle to each on a table, my room with its coals by the fireside, I ponder these questions. And as I do, the tank starts to dissolve in the infinite ambiguity of life. I have to name it 'tank' simply to keep a hold on it. Despite this, the more realistic visions break out now and then with their incontrovertible posting. There is one which fascinates me. I see a misty…intestinal seething, in which there is something else, more static and tense, composed of harder angles. I can watch this almost as I watch the coals on the fire, a continually shifting formation in which there is something constant. The nature of the constant is something I should know. It is what I attempt to know but cannot with complete directness. I am like a scientist, reduced to deducting it from what it is that I can see and put into words. There is a science for it. I am a rheologist. I study the deformation and flow of surfaces. I am as before, though, in danger of being mesmerised by the vision itself, dreaming the incandescent constant as an astronomer watching the sun, as the discovery of a mystery. Some enjoyment however is a useful motivation. I am not an ascetic and I could not easily be of this century if I were. It would be a lie. Difficult as the parody is, it is an avoidance of the more important risk. I admit rather than deny myself. However, in the nature of my commitment there is something severe, a self, not decaying, but judging in order to change … something, so a denying of a self, a selflessness. Then I can just say, that even in my enjoyment, if I enjoy myself as part of the attempt, there is an ascetic quality.

Then I am alone. Why? If not an ascetic, why? I am too ugly, too violent? In a sense, perhaps. My wife has left me? No. Then through alienation? I am not sure. No, I am alone because beyond the truth that I am with is the truth that I am alone. I am alone because stripped of the diverting swish of people and events, stripped of the illusory extension of myself which they form, I am what is left and there I am responsible. It is the starting point for optimism. It is through myself that I make discoveries, in it that I find the world, even if I find it difficult to interpret what I know. I built the tank in the first place. I am alone because it is a characteristic of this century, the disbanding that has arisen, through the relentless destruction of certainties, in which there is so much hope as well as so much danger. It is only when we can live with uncertainty and welcome it in that we can be truly adult. The only certainty is in grasping life continually as if for the first, not merely knowing it but feeling it. This is the creative truth. It is difficult to say the word 'alone' because it brings with its utterance a call for sympathy or pity and its negation, a need which I am still weak enough to assert for myself. Knowing the associations of it, I find myself saying the words tremulously. I am alone with sentimentality or loneliness.

So alone in my room. What are the details of it? I am alone with the coal fire which subdues and pacifies me. And it would be dishonest for it not to be there. There is this warmth and homeliness which I cannot ignore. I cannot deny that there is comfort. Genuinely I appreciate it, distrustful as I am of it. But the coal fire is hedged around with cautions. I view it at times as a lost innocence, glowing with a child-like trust, a medicine which, though still effective, is insufficient to meet the demands placed upon it. How well does it stand up to the building of boron tetrafluoride, or the construction of high-rise flats? The only murders it sanctions are those which have romance. The knife and the box – less wonderful – I feel more easy with. They are a means of luxury which don't have the autonomy of fire, the autonomy of vision, they are at my service and under my control. They lie, plain and unfanciful, ready for innumerable simple acts. I feel a fondness for them. They are more sensible. Other objects define my room. The record player which puts side by side the cries and murmurings of the human, with the also insubstantial jerking of electrons. The books I have bought with their fictional theorisings to read once or not at all and then walk into the street. Various implements of living. And then the room.

The room is one of the primary areas where life is expounded, concentrating atmosphere to a degree which elsewhere only comes through the frame of violence or detachment. It also concentrates humans on what is best, worst, what is most persistent in them, that with which they agree. It is the place where people are most self-conscious, knowing that each word is heard and that they have least excuse of deflection in how they present themselves. It is where people are both at their easiest and their most awkward.

Even my room must suffer by not merely being there. How can I live in this world of abstractions? I forget myself. It comes from living too much in this room. I covet this living. Only by its means can I live as I do. For I am in this room in order to reflect, to construct the street in which I will live, that is its purpose. It is my laboratory, and the artefacts of it dirty the fieldwork of observation to yield erroneous results. Even on the plateau where I sometimes lie to relax there is the impropriety of this examining, and I speak as if I am in a room. Fortunately, in the scenes which are important to me, this negligence is driven out by the straitening effects of confrontation. No, I do submit to the room of walls and a ceiling, the room where books are read by a coal fire. I can leave behind the violence and its jealous claim upon the room. Then, if I need a likeness to mar the contentedness by, it is a likening of the room to a cabin, as adrift in the exhilarating swell of the people-ocean. I am calm and fresh but the moments are rare. I try to take with me the seashell for these moments. My nostalgia is like this shell.

History interests me. Here is the grand sameness, the one which unites whole continents. Interests me because whatever is studied in history, its means of pain are not obsolescent. They crouch grinning in the unspoken connotations of words, of attitudes, of physical bearing. Walking along the street I participate in genocides and crusades, perhaps especially these two, in royal regattas… What I know would fill endless books if only I could articulate or illustrate myself. So I am naïve. I cannot be. Millennia of history enter into even my pettiest bickering, into even my naivety because I suspect that I must have come to speak like this. The thought of what I am convulses me with laughter. How is it possible to take what I am with an appropriate gravity? I could not live. Each word and thought would be too heavy. I must be found more insubstantial if there is to be an act. There must be some blindness: it is healthy that people do not know who they speak to and are not so self-conscious. Or do we fully realise without words this truth in the moment of meeting? In either way, there is an obligation for an intolerable respect for humans and, with the knowledge, a burden of courage in approaching one. I require this bravery in order to approach the tank. The bravery can be more light-hearted, though. I laugh sometimes to see the mischievousness of the approach; confronted by the grumbling severity of the millennia, an approach that digs it – whatever it is – in the ribs and tells it to shut up, holds a party around its toes as the giant roars miles above. History reduces us to children.

To the extent that we merely contain history we have complicity. We are to blame. But solutions? I am not as good at solutions. I juggle feverishly with the answer that there can only be more of the same. I try to take advantage of the situation to substitute a different ball and practise sleight of hand. That is the real test of my understanding, how good a juggler or magician I am.

Somehow we live as if for the first, have to necessarily. And this is the deception which creativity is. In it we convince ourselves of life; have, as in painting a picture, an underlying certainty felt almost as a compulsion – and that is the creative truth we need in order to live. In each brush stroke, there is risk and uncertainty. As in front of the tank, the painting concentrates living but it is too easily an alternative to life. All commitment is a creativity and it is a way of coping with uncertainty. It has a breathtaking, literal, ignorance: to acknowledge this history, this certain means of uncertainty, but ignore it. Perhaps this approaches adulthood as practically as it can be achieved. There is still something childish. In a commitment which increases uncertainty and indefiniteness, there is more adulthood. Then I have a fear that to be truly adult requires a state of immobility, crippled by the weight of what one knows. Adherence to convention gives a good impression of maturity.

The study of history is appropriate to the position of being alone in a room, and with history I am not so lonely. In my unfreedom I am not lonely, many people cling to me, the shaggy fur overcoat of history pursues me. I am anyway not so alone. The room is appropriate, for what is history – other than a succession of decisions to put the house in order, followed by a desire for a new 'living room'. This is history, glorious and domestic! Everything is here in this room through the circle of associations which engulfs the world as it moves away from me. In the inner part of the circle there is again a city. What is a city?

It is a city of tourists. The city has parks, buildings, exhibitions. There is some litter and dirt, a few tramps and hooligans maybe. No! The city is built on layers of excrement, on layers of corpses and discarded objects. The richness of life is the richness of this stench. The pride of the city, the pride of life. Come down into this mess where we really live and then we can begin to talk. People walk like tourists, faces that don't face up to this, walk as moving points, dragging in each step an immense swamp, moving in the fresh air at the top of the pyramid. They are like the sailors who used to land on the backs of monsters, thinking they were the natural wonder of a floating island. A sabre cut would have revealed that the water was thick and warm.

I struggle to keep alive the naivety which is required to act, the optimism and sense of freedom. Not to confuse it with the tendency to walk through this submerged civilisation like a tourist, the temptation to be too easily free. Yes, I know there have been carefree and brilliant moments. The history seems dark primarily because it is something which has happened without our being fully conscious of it. The insidiousness of life! It is like a trauma. By the time I am conscious of it, it is difficult to move. Standing in front of the tank, almost, I am just there, sustained by the fascination of composing these suicide notes. I am too heavy with the weight of civilisation. It is the heaviness which will stop me. The simple act of stepping out into the open. I am too heavy...................

I am nearing the end of what I have to say. I have my doubts about what I have said. Sometimes I think I betray a glorification of war, a need for it, in the excitement I express, in the time I devote to it and in the colour with which I surround it. Sometimes I think it is myself I glorify. I am weak. I stray from the point all of the time. While I do not claim to be a deeply spiritual person, I am aware of a need to be, for all of us to be, if we are to avert disaster or stand up to it. But I have hope. In my thinking, the spiritual is a quality which can develop with time. The question is whether we have enough time. I am dubious but I still hope.

I will leave you with a story. It is an optimistic story; you may not believe it but still I hope you like it.

Once there was a kingdom, or rather a queendom, called Onomatopoeia. It was not a bad queendom. None of its people were rich but then none of them were poor. They worked hard and lived in reasonable comfort and generally with well-being. The laws were not harsh, indeed they were quite enlightened. The punishment for an offender was to work helping the victim of the crime for a period, or if that was not acceptable, to work in the public service. There were others, socially advanced laws, which would have been better if they had been adhered to without obligation but were nevertheless helpful to the society. For instance, people were obliged by law to clear the snow in front of their house. If a neighbour was ill, they were obliged to help the neighbour, or do the work the neighbour could not do. The care of old people was an obligation in law. However, the people were not perfect; there was crime and so there was a force of police. But as the laws they enforced were just, the people regarded them with friendliness and because of the good repu-tation of the police, people of high principle joined the force. The knowl-edge of the people was advanced in some ways – they had timepieces, for instance. There were public libraries and art galleries, all writers and artists were employed by the Queen as few people could afford to buy or print their products. There was music and dancing and frequent holidays during which to experience them. There were schools in which much time was spent helping the children to learn morality and to develop their feeling for others. Then there was the Queen. She had magical powers and could heal people. Also she could do more obviously dramatic things. On holidays she sometimes used to give displays of coloured fireballs which darted about in the air above the heads of the watchers. She had a palace of sorts, but most of it consisted of a large hall in which representa-tives of the people met, under her guidance, to pass laws or discuss them. She herself lived in two rooms to one side of the hall. People could come and talk to her at any time. One day as she was musing by herself in the hall, a messenger rushed in.

'Your majesty, the Hasslebadians are going to invade us! They have decided that they are going to "bestow on us the privilege of their form of government".'

'Oh dear,' said the Queen.

The Hasslebadians were a strange people. A few of them were very rich indeed and they were rich because they owned the people of their country, who were made to work all the hours of waking and very hard too. The people had none of the fruits of their labour, except for two bowls of porridge and an apple each day, which was decreed by law as the obligation of the master towards his slave. However, this could be with-held for various reasons – if the slave was found resting, for instance. Punishments were severe, and for stealing a pitcher of milk a person could be executed. The nobility of Hasslebad were quite convinced that this form of government was right, they were quite idealistic about it and, unfortunately, a fair number of their subjects agreed with them. 'We get our porridge, after all,' was their comment. In case of discontent, and to further their wish to conquer, the Hasslebad nobility kept an army. The men in the army were relatively well paid: it would be a risk to have a discontented army. So the army of Hasslebad marched into Onomatopoeia one day. As the soldiers were convinced of the selflessness and correctness of what they did, they expected to be welcomed as heroes, a liberating force, a force of progress. However, they were in error. When the messenger had left the Queen she had sent a telepathic message to all the people of Onomatopoeia.

'Whatever they ask you to do, don't do it. Hide your money and valuables in the earth. Be prepared for punishment, even death. They cannot kill us all.' She gave other details.

The Queen herself changed her clothes and went to live in an ordinary house. The Treasurer and the few other officials did the same, burying the documents of state in their gardens. The first act of the invading army was to search for the Queen; they intended to make her the puppet ruler, as they thought that the people would obey her with less trouble. They could not find her, having never seen her before, only having heard of her. They tried to loot the Treasury, only to find that there were no valuables in it – the art galleries likewise. And as all the officials who looked after these concerns had vanished, they had no-one to torture and from whom to extract the information of their whereabouts. The army tried a few public executions to compel the officials through altruism, but these had no effect.

A soldier would ask an Onomatopoeian the time. The Onomatopoeian would refuse to give it. The soldier would demand the person's watch. The Onomatopoeian would smash it on the ground. The soldier would be late for his duty and be reprimanded. When a soldier was sent to interrogate someone, that person would not speak to him. He demanded that the person come with him to army headquarters. The Onomatopoeian sat on the ground. It was impossible to shift them. The soldier had to go and get help. When they got to headquarters, the Onomatopoeian still wouldn't say anything. Under torture, he or she would confess to having received a message through the ether and the soldiers found this to be the case with all their victims. There was no ringleader they could identify.

The Hasslebad leaders started to produce new laws. They demanded that the citizens assemble in crowds to hear them but no-one did. They tried to have posters printed but the printers and printing press had disappeared. They found one printer but obviously they could not kill him, otherwise they would never be able to print. They went to the iron foundry and demanded a printing press but mysteriously, the plans for one had disappeared, as had their originator. They were on the point of imprisoning the metal workers when it struck them that they were necessary for their operations in Onomatopoeia and that, after all, it saved the expense if the Onomatopoeians bought their own ploughshares and oxen rather than having to be given them. Thus a measure of independence was achieved.

Soldiers were ordered to carry out the laborious duty of knocking on every door in the country and explaining the new laws. By some mysterious arrangement, no-one answered their doors, which greatly puzzled the soldiers. The truth was simple if one only knew the correct rhythm to knock. They were forced to stop people in the streets and tell them but this was difficult: a number of soldiers were necessary, as the Onomatopoeians did not stay to listen unless they were forced; but even then, the soldiers could be absolutely certain that none of the information would be passed on. As there were so many faces to remember, it was impossible to accost a person and charge them with not having told others as instructed. Few of the soldiers knew the Onomatopoeian language and no-one would teach them, so a very few soldiers were forced to great labours.

It was clear that a knowledge of the law would take months, if not years, to instil. The Hasslebadian leaders sent back to Hasslebad for printed posters which arrived after about six weeks. These were posted up in the towns and villages. They were painted over and scratched out. More were sent for. This time a soldier was stationed by each poster throughout the country. No-one could read them.

The Hasslebadians did not have watches or clocks in their country so they decided to denude the watchmaker's shop of its wares but they realised that if they did, the watchmaker would go out of business and there would be no more watches and clocks. It was a foregone conclusion that he would not work for them, even on the threat of death. They contented themselves with taking the occasional timepiece. A number of businesses achieved independence in this way.

The food shops escaped as well. The Hasslebadians lived almost exclusively on meat, whereas the Onomatopoeians lived on vegetables. The Hasslebadians sent back to Hasslebad for sheep and cattle, which arrived after about a month. There was a problem, however. The whole country was covered with fields in which there were at most a few vegetables at this time of year, or else the fields were ploughed and bare. The animals had to be kept in the hills on the outskirts of the country. As no Onomatopoeian would help them, the soldiers were forced to build shepherd's huts. Onomatopoeians were given the task of looking after the animals and carried bodily out to them. The animals wandered off and were lost, some to the powerful country of Agorophobia into which the Hasslebadians dared not trespass, and others were eaten by wolves. The Onomatopoeians were executed. Soldiers were sent out to replace them. Even so, great numbers of animals mysteriously went missing. Eventually, the attempt was given up. Convoys of animals were sent to Hasslebad when and as needed.

As all the wealth of the country had been hidden and no amount of threat would induce the people to reveal it, the Hasslebadians decided to work the silver mines and carry off this booty. They rounded many hundreds of Onomatopoeians together and drove them, or rather carried them, to the silver mines. The Onomatopoeians refused to work. One was whipped. He still refused. Eventually he was unfit to work anyway. They tried another. The same response and so on. Finally, they gave up. They decided to imprison the people but there was a problem: there were no prisons in Onomatopoeia; they had to be built.

Whatever the threats, no Onomatopoeians would help them. The soldiers had to build the prisons themselves. The silver mines were mined but the people with the skills necessary to process the ore had disappeared. The ore was taken back to Hasslebad in cartloads. Finally all the ore was extracted. The Hasslebadians wondered how best to secure their arms.

The Hasslebadians had executed a great many people by now and it came to them that the resistance was so solid that they could go on killing until the whole people had been killed. Then there would be no slaves. The killing ceased except for exceptional cases. Imprisonment was the course taken. The prisons swelled until a great proportion of the Onomatopoeians were in them. The Hasslebadians were worried. If everyone was put in prison there would be no-one to act as slaves. One or two of the Hasslebadians voiced the opinion that the attempt should be given up. The Onomatopoeians willingly sent vegetables to the prison.

Throughout this period, music and dancing continued. Mysteriously, at apparently appointed times, throngs of people gathered in the streets of squares. The coloured fireballs danced in the air, the music played. Frequently the soldiers were sent to disperse these demonstrations of independence but finally they gave up; it would have been necessary to imprison the whole population.

The Hasslebadians considered sowing grass in all the farmlands and using the grass for grazing. But by now it was evident that no Onomatopoeian would help them. They would have to import workers from Hasslebad. This raised a question. What was the advantage of it? Either the Hasslebad slaves worked in Hasslebad to make wealth for their masters, or they worked in Onomatopoeia. What was the difference? The wealth was the same and then it was not ideal to live so far from the Hasslebad capital, the King and court, the activities. If people and soldiers were sent here, Hasslebad would be more vulnerable to attack, there would not be so many people to defend Hasslebad. It was a foregone conclusion that the Onomatopoeians would not fight for them.

Why not kill the whole useless people of Onomatopoeia? If they wouldn't work as slaves, what use were they? But then what use would it serve to kill them? The Hasslebadians were not totally without reasoning powers. They would trade with them instead. Suddenly, one day the army of Hasslebad packed up and left for Hasslebad.

The story carried to Agorophobia, Claustrophobia and all the surrounding countries and consequently the other countries knew that it was useless to try to annexe Onomatopoeia. The Onomatopoeians lived in peace for many centuries.

I made beauty
where before was
ugliness
I made a living
where before
was waste
I made a dwelling
where before was dereliction
I made the best
where before
was not the best

I made something
out of nothing
which is a bit like
being a god.

ॐ

Appendix

THE MYSTERIOUS MARBLER

For some of you who read this article books may be an article of commerce; for others, objects of rarity and value. Others may be fired by an aesthetic sense or a love of old books. There will be historians and lovers of literature. But, how many of you take notice of the by now faded and scuffed marbled paper which adorns your books? This is the first thing which my eyes seek out.

The title for my article comes from an advertisement in a trade journal of the last century. Even as a practitioner of marbling what I do seems mysterious to me at times, although the basic principles can be described fairly simply. The origins of marbling have also been something of a mystery, and our present knowledge is a good example of how much closer to the past we have become in our sense of time and understanding.

Reading the literature on marbling, writers have attributed the origin of the art to a number of different countries. Holland, France, Germany, Turkey and Iran have all been suggested as the birthplace. Today, the publicity of an Italian marbler suggests that the invention was that of Mace Ruette, a royal bookbinder in the time of King Louis the Thirteenth of France. The truth seems to be that marbling was first practised in Turkey, although I believe that in the Victoria and Albert Museum's manuscript room there is a twelfth century Iranian manuscript with what appears to be marbling on its border. The gum tragacanth which was originally used to make the marbling medium is grown in Turkey, and it is still possible to obtain sheets of 'Ebru' as it is called, although it is very much a dying art there. Apparently, in Turkey it was possible to go to the marbler and ask him to write the name of God in marbling; floral designs were also quite popular as decorations in houses. It is peculiar that marbling's origins should have become so obscure when the English philosopher and inventor Francis Bacon actually writes of a Turkish origin at a time when the art had not yet become popular in this country. With this Middle Eastern origin in mind, there seems a certain correctness that a group of marbled pictures I made should have been bought to decorate the conference centre of the Bahai religion in this country.

There is, apart from the art we know, an art developed (presumably independently) in Japan, the art of Sumingagachi which has the same basic principles but is very much different in appearance. Traditionally, Sumingagachi consists of concentric rings of the same delicate colour, looking perhaps like the contour lines of a map, as opposed to western marbling which can resemble marble in a loose way.

When I say to a non-bookman that I make marbled paper, there are two inevitable questions: 'What is it?' 'How is it made?' Here I will concern myself with the second question.

I have been asked whether I paint the paper by hand, but it would take a very skilled and meticulous painter to produce in a week's work what marbling can do in a few seconds. Or do I print the paper? It is possible to buy printed marble paper, but it is easy to tell that it has been printed. Towards the end of the last century rollers with marbled designs in relief were produced for marbling book edges, but again, the effect is inferior to real marbling. Marbling is done by floating water based colours on a viscous size which is usually made by boiling Carragheen Moss seaweed. Paper coated with a mordant, which is traditionally alum, is laid down on the surface of the size and when the paper is removed, all the colours stick to the paper. The paper is then washed to remove surplus size and hung to up to dry. The dried paper can be treated in various ways, by wax polishing, by gelatinising which produces a high gloss finish, or by coating the paper with glue-size and then ironing it, which is what I do.

The last treatment protects the colours from rubbing and damp, and leaves a slight patina on the surface. The colours would ordinarily sink when thrown on to the surface of the size, but a few drops of surfactant are added to the paint which makes it spread out to an extent which can be controlled by the marbler. Traditionally this is ox-gall, but spirit of soap, egg yolk, Fairy Liquid(!) or a solution of shellac with borax in water can be used. It is possible to marble just on water, but the colours tend to drift around uncontrollably and make it impossible to achieve good results. Gum tragacanth or Gun Dragon, which I have mentioned before, provides a very good marbling medium and is used by a French marbler called Michel Duval. However, it is a bit too expensive for casual use. When the colour has been thrown on to the size, it may be manipulated in various ways. A stylus drawn through a spot, for instance, transforms it into a line, and a surface of lines can be combed to produce the feathered effect that is so common in marbling. Other combs can be used to produce curls or the little-seen (on antiquarian books) pattern called 'peacock' which has a resemblance to a mass of peacocks' feathers. A more accessible version of marbling can be tried easily, and this is to float oil-based colours on water, as quite a number of children have done at school. This will produce a gaily coloured swirling pattern which may look good on a notebook. If you would like to try the more traditional technique, paints and a small booklet on marbling are available from Dryad Handicrafts of Leicester and Carragheen Moss can be ordered through any herbalist.

Marbled paper was first used in this country in the seventeenth century. The first patterns to be produced were of a simple design known as 'Old Dutch', which resembles the marbling that used to be done on the edges of ledgers, except that the combed stripes are narrower. As the name suggests, this pattern originated in Holland, and the story goes that it was introduced to this country as wrapping paper on goods to avoid a tax on paper that was in existence at the time. 'Stormont' became very popular, and this is the pattern where indigo spots are riddled with hundreds of tiny holes. It is made by adding turpentine to the colour, and I am attempting to find a way of producing this once-common pattern; with modern materials you are very lucky indeed if you can produce it. 'French Shell' became very popular at the beginning of the nineteenth century and onwards, and this is the pattern where the spots of the top layer of paint are shaded, more dense in colour toward the centre.

Every trade that has been carried out for a long time has its own terms and names for processes and products involved; these are often a way of humanising the trade and encoding the practitioner's feeling for it. Other patterns are called 'Gloster', 'Italian', 'Spanish,' 'Antique Spot', 'Turkish' and there are more. For example Spanish is produced by rocking the paper backwards and forwards as it is laid down on the size from one corner, and the result is paper with ripples on it as if the pattern is seen under water. This is a more recent development, being popular especially toward the end of the nineteenth century. It is amongst my patterns, but I mention it really for the story that it was supposed to have been the invention of a marbler who came back drunk after lunch and couldn't deal with the paper in the ordinary way! It is possible.

For anyone who would like to investigate the history of marbling further, I would recommend two works which may be hard to come by. The first is a treatise called *The Whole Art of Marbling* by C.W.Woolnough, published in 1881. Although written instructions are not enough to produce good marbling, this is the most complete guide available. It is a beautiful book as every other page is an actual piece of marbled paper. It is possible to get a copy to read through the public library system. The other is *The Art of Marbling* by Josef Halfer, produced at the turn of the century. St Bride's Institute of Fleet Street in London has a wealth of material and the staff are very helpful.

I myself first became interested in marbling through working in an antiquarian bookshop, where the resident bibliographer said to me: 'Whoever took up marbling would do well for themselves,' and so I took up marbling, at first, over the bath and sink, and gradually taking it more seriously. The turning point came one day when I cycled past a derelict public lavatory which had a 'To Let' notice on it. I wondered whether the

'i' had been left out but I went to the council all the same. Bemused council officials and workmen came with me and broke into the boarded-up building, where I wandered through the rubble saying that it was just what I wanted. I was given the place rent free for two years in exchange for making it good. At the time I was working as a cleaner in a medieval hall in York, and as my workshop was in a street called Melrosegate, the Custodian at the hall suggested that I call myself 'Melrosegate Fancy Papers' and the name stuck. I found by trial and error how to marble properly and the business took off. It shows how word spreads in the book world that I didn't need to advertise myself once, and in no time at all I had enough orders to give up my part-time job and be a marbler. I had just started on a facsimile paper for the British Museum when to my great regret I had to abandon the business for personal reasons, but from Michael Sessions of Quacks Printers in York came an offer of a workshop fitted out to my requirements and it is from this workshop that I have run my business.

This article was originally published in the Antiquarian Book Monthly Review, *August 1987.*

'I was impressed by your marble paper…the quality and stability of the marbling was extremely good… The pattern you have used would be very popular with our binders. There are very few highly skilled crafts-men like yourself who are producing papers of a good quality… I hope that some time in the future you will be able to continue with your craft.'
In a letter from Chris Smith, Conservation Manager, The British Library, May 1997.

See pages 82-84 for Mark's description of himself at work in his workshop (photo below).

MARK WHITTAKER 1956 – 2003

ark was born in 1956 in Burton-on-Trent. His brother Adrian was born there four years earlier, in 1952. Mark was just five when he moved to Blackheath, South-East London. When he was about ten, he joined the choir of the local church and eventually became lead choirboy. He was being trained to sing his first solo just after his thirteenth birthday when, two days before the event, the choirmaster realised with consternation that Mark's voice had broken. However, sing he did, with a little discreet help over the high notes. It was the passage from Handel based on the words 'How beautiful upon the mountains are the feet that preach the gospel of peace.' He always wished to teach the gospel of peace; hated war and militarism and actively supported peace organisations.

At Crown Woods Comprehensive school he was an all-rounder: he had colours for both hockey and rugby, a judo belt, sang with the choir and had his first sight of Scotland when the choir went for a fortnight's training session at a lodge in Inverliever. He played trombone in the school orchestra and had lessons in piano at the Blackheath Conservatoire. There was a large and interesting sixth form at his school and he and his friends formed a band, 'Cosmic Heroes', in which he played saxophone and harmonica.

As a child he was always interested in nature – birds, butterflies, flowers and stones. He never went to the beach on holidays in Pembrokeshire without a hammer to look for fossils. He designed a pigeon loft, which his father helped him build, and was the youngest member by far of the Greenwich pigeon club.

In his middle years at school, in a period timetabled for recreational cultural activities (enlightened days, those) Mark opted to make a Cement Fondue head; the school found a local sculptor to help him. His family dubbed the figure 'Ozymandias' and he now sits inside the hedge of his mother's front garden on the first spot the removal men could drop him.

Walking became a favourite pastime; over the years he walked the South Downs Way, Offa's Dyke, Hadrian's Wall, The Pennine Way, and round Northern and Western Scotland. He later said that the happiest time of his life was when walking alone in the Scottish Mountains.

At York University he joined an ecology group which designed a Geodesic dome with a windmill to go beside it and applied formally for a grant and permission to build it. However, work on his Biochemistry degree intervened and the project lapsed. He was also part of the York Anarchist group. A group of his friends also worked to support people on the margins, including a young schizophrenic man and later a young woman. After graduation Mark stayed in York when the others dispersed and took on a great deal of the burden himself.

He had found himself a piano teacher and began working for the Performance grade. She found him a few young pupils and he did various they jobs – several weeks on an archaeological dig, assistant Custodian at a Medieval Hall – and with an antiquarian book dealer, which was where he became interested in marbling. He managed to locate a rare Victorian treatise, *The Whole Art of Marbling*, and experimented over the bath and the sink. One day, spotting from his bicycle a disused public lavatory on a small piece of waste land, he approached the council and won permission to convert it into a workshop, and set about it until he became an excellent marbler. The business quickly took off; word spread through the bookbinding world and orders flowed. The mixture of art and science was what had attracted him to the process and he planned to make a career of it.

Mark had written poetry at school, but it was in this same period, the early Eighties in York, that the bulk of the material in this book was composed; he wrote many short stories and poems and two books – one a meditation on militarism and pacifism (Approach to the Threshold), the other a picaresque novel (Search for the Holy Grail) which drew on his knowledge of a range of York subcultures. He had an offer to publish this, subject to some reworking, but did not go on with it as he felt friends might recognise themselves too easily as characters.

It was while working on an order for The British Museum – during a very hot summer, which made the process more difficult – that he had a schizophrenic breakdown. There followed some years when he was backwards and forwards between York and his parents in Saffron Walden. He tried to set up another workshop in York but, after some difficult times, had to sell his house and return to Saffron Walden, eventually being transferred to the care of the Fulbourn Hospital outreach psychiatrist – though he was very wary of institutions and medication. After some years with his parents and a brief stay in Fulbourn, Mark moved into sheltered accommodation in Station Street, Saffron Walden, which he helped to make feel as much like a York communal house as it could be. He felt secure there, changed his medication and gradually became less unhappy and much more accepting of his life.

The bulk of Mark's writing stems from the early 1980s, but in Saffron Walden he continued his religious searchings (adopting the name of 'Marak'), wrote many short pieces and poems and felt he had achieved 'divine self realisation'. He felt much less troubled and anxious; he became more outgoing again and very clear that Station Street was, for the time being, the best place to be. The care and love of the staff there gave him a real sense of security.

In 2002 he developed what seemed to be Petit Mal epilepsy, but between attacks he often seemed almost well again, his quirky sense of humour in evidence; he also became more able to have two-way relationships. In October 2003 he died suddenly of an epileptic seizure.

Hilda and Adrian Whittaker

MARK WHITTAKER'S POEMS

ark Whittaker's poems are deeply rooted in nature, and express a timeless spirituality. This is the world in its natural state, despite the ravages of people and 'progress'. If you know how to look, innocence, romance, mystery and simple joys can still be found: 'Alone amongst the mountains man can have dignity,' Mark says. The poems draw on literary, mythological and psychological sources, the preoccupation with love and nature of the metaphysical poets and the pre-industrial concerns of the Romantics. Innocence is not naivety, however. The poems explore the gentleness of life but also its darker forces.

The poems celebrate the vibrancy and power of being alive, as in 'The woman has come'. 'Star-freckled and ginger-eyed', from this poem, is one of my favourite images. Love is transcendent as well as sexual and the poems deal with the interconnectedness of love and nature, the divine essences and universal laws. There is a strong visual element, particularly the painterly imagery of 'The Snake Charmer', where not only colour but also texture, light and shade call to mind a Pre-Raphaelite painting. Amongst the 'London' poems, Mark takes a fond and somewhat bemused look at himself as a child – was this small innocent person really me? In the 'York' section, 'Fulford Cemetery' stands out as a celebratory poem.

Other poems, in contrast, deal with more specific events and aspects of Mark's experience and employ a more complex interaction of ideas and imagery. These convey a darker, less optimistic feel, mourning the loss of innocence rather than celebrating simple joys (such as 'I am a stranger'). Mark also shows the vulnerability and fragility of the innocent state, the exposed soul in the 'House of Cards', having to deal with the harshness of life: 'I was fragile on the people-ocean where pirates roamed.' In 'Birth' the innocent baby is menaced into a state of powerlessness as soon as it makes its first appearance in this world. Mark explores the social construct of 'normality' in his poem 'My Sister'. 'I am not ashamed,' says the woman in defence of her femaleness. Freud is regarded here as one of a long line of culprits attempting to legitimise the persecution of women in their natural state. These darker poems seem to be saying that it is only possible to be truly alive in our world by being 'mad'. There are references to death and destruction, the desire for oblivion in 'tangle me in seaweeds and corals' and 'close your eyes the eagle says, and be happy that you will not return'.

This is a powerful and inspired collection.

Since his death in 2003, Mark's poems have acquired an even greater poignancy:

'When life has passed
Death sentence;
What man may survive?
I have done.'

Deborah Cole (June 2004)

SIDELIGHTS

Mark's names

After his breakdown, Mark devised many different names for himself. His favourite in recent years was 'Marak'.

The names 'I have made for myself' are:
Marakå
Marak Saffron Walden
Mavråshdi
Marak
The Mahavira Marak
Sri Marak
Mark Alban Whittaker
Yaxcat
M.A.W.
Mark

Mark's jokebook

However unwell Mark felt at times, he always retained an idiosyncratic and quirky sense of humour and delighted in writing, collecting and telling jokes. Here are a few from one of his several jokebooks:

Q. What's green and goes up and down?
A. A gooseberry in a lift.

Q. Where do baby monkeys sleep?
In an apricot.

Q. Why did the beetroot blush?
A. Because it saw the salad dressing.

Q. What is shepherd's pie?
A. Twenty-two sheep jumping over seven hedges.

Q. How many psychiatrists does it take to change a lightbulb?
A. One, but the lightbulb has got to really want to change.

Q. How many lightbulbs does it take to change a psychiatrist?

Sign in a hospital car park: 'Warning – Thieves Operate In This Car Park.'
Graffiti: 'Why – aren't there enough surgeons?'

A schizophrenic: 'I created the world.'
A nurse, sadly: 'That explains why it's all such a mess.'

Elephant to mouse: 'You're very small.'
Mouse: 'Well, I've been very ill.'

The Four Laws Of Schizophrenia

(See The Four Laws Of Robotics – I. Asimov)

1. Don't let the bastards get you down.
2. Not much money in schizophrenia these days.
3. Oh well, there's some good laughs sometimes.
4. Some schizophrenics are the best people there are.

'Mark Whittaker, (relatively but formally) BA Hons. Biochemistry.'

Mark's take on life

In the last years of his life, Mark spent a lot of time developing a comprehensive personal philosophy. In doing this, he was trying to make sense of his illness and pass on to others what he had learnt from nearly twenty years of 'mental dis-ease', as he termed it. He produced a variety of small booklets of thoughts, aphorism and prayers. Here are some excerpts:

Government
Government, in some meaning of the term, is the cause of militarism. And militarism is a crime against humanity. Therefore a gentle anarchism is the only way to peace. Strictly, anarchism means 'no government' – but positively, a kind of ideal state of existence whereby coercion and the rule of law are unnecessary due to people's mature social being.

Mental illness
There are not many psychological conditions which cannot be made a great deal better by love, the right environment, enough money, the right people, prayer, analysis, counselling and spiritual work. Rejection feelings are very important in mental dis-ease; the feeling that people don't like me can lead to the feeling that people are getting at me, paranoia; if I'm rejected it's because I must have done something to deserve it, guilt.

For people susceptible to mental dis-ease physical work is a very good idea to get the sufferer out of their head and into their body more. Exposure to beauty of all kinds is a good idea, to contradict the feeling of inner ugliness that sufferers have and to counteract the perception of the world as a cruel and ugly place.

Adversity
It is a wonderful ability to laugh in the face of adversity or, poetically speaking, death, as this is to be stronger than adversity or death in a small way. It is possible.

Aphorisms
People are happiest when they have true freedom.
Be good-natured.
The inspired strength of goodness.
The loving nourishment of one's bodily being.
Love one another with pure heart fervently.

Beauty is the mother of truth.
Lies are the servants of tyrants.
Colourfulness of character is important.
Don't lose your marbles!

Prayers

O my true Lord God, please let me go with complete ease to the beauteous realm of the beyond forever, when I should.

O my true Lord God, let all true gains for goodness in my own life never be lost.

My two prayers
despite anything.